SPECIAL NEEDS

h a n d b o o k   f o r

HEALTH & SOCIAL CARE

Carolyn Meggitt

Hodder
A MEMBER OF THE HODDER HEADLINE GROUP

Acknowledgements

I would like to acknowledge Jessica Stevens, lecturer in child care and education at Northampton College, for her help and encouragement; Doris Belbin, Day Care Manager at White Gables in Bromley, Kent, for information on Alzheimer's disease; Martin and Alayne Levy for the biography of their daughter Hannah in Chapter 4; Peter Bailey, Manager of The Avenue Day Centre in Teddington, Middlesex, for information on service provision in Chapter 6; Richard Kember for providing a case study; Mark and Stacey Croucher and their son, Jack, for providing the photographs on pages 8 and 199; Elisabeth Tribe, Anna Clark and Llinos Edwards at Hodder & Stoughton for their support.

I would also like to thank my family, Dave, Jonathan, Leo and Laura, for their support and forbearance during my writing hours.

This book is dedicated to my mother, Gwen Hayward MBE, who has
Parkinson's disease.

The publishers would like to thank the following for reproduction of copyright material: Julian Calder/Impact, fig 3.2; Lupe Kunhe, fig 3.3; Isabel Lilly/RNIB, fig 3.14; Crisis, fig 4.8; the Boots Company plc and Coopers Healthcare, figs 5.1–5.6, 5.12–5.16. 'Do Unto Others' by Janice Pink, reprinted on page 17 from *Mustn't Grumble* edited by Lois Keith, first published by The Women's Press Ltd, 1994, 34 Great Sutton Street, London EC1V 0DX, is used by permission of The Women's Press Ltd. 'Stolen Feelings' by Andrew Gregan, reprinted on pages 73 and 74 is reproduced with the permission of *The Guardian*.

A catalogue record for this title is available from The British Library

ISBN 0 340 683600

First published 1997
Impression number   10 9 8 7 6 5 4 3 2 1
Year   2002 2001 2000 1999 1998 1997

Copyright © 1997, Carolyn Meggitt

Typeset by Wearset, Boldon, Tyne and Wear.
Printed in Great Britain for Hodder & Stoughton Educational, a division of Hodder Headline Plc, 338 Euston Road, London NW1 3BH by Scotprint, Musselburgh, Scotland.

Contents

CHAPTER 1

BASIC HUMAN NEEDS

This chapter outlines basic human needs, using Maslow's hierarchy as a model. These needs are: physical, intellectual, emotional, social, cultural, spiritual, sexual, giving, receiving, exploring, finding out, taking risks. The main focus is on the needs which are present after the most basic needs for survival have been met. These needs are universal; no matter what our physical condition, we all have the same basic needs.

There are certain universal needs which are common to all individuals, whatever their circumstances. Any study of plant and animal biology will describe the needs which must be met to ensure the survival of an organism. In human terms, such basic needs are extended to take into account the complexity of human life. It is not enough to consider purely physical needs such as food, warmth, shelter and water; we need to consider the basic requirements for a life of fulfilment and personal worth.

Basic human needs have been defined by Maslow as:

- to have sufficient appropriate food and drink
- to eliminate waste products
- to breathe properly
- to have the body at a comfortable temperature
- to sleep and rest
- to keep clean and maintain health
- to wear suitable clothing
- to communicate and interact with others
- to be free from discomfort and pain
- to feel safe.

Maslow's hierarchy of needs

Abraham Maslow (1908–70) devised a hierarchy of needs from which, he believed, all our motivations arise. These needs are usually represented in pyramid

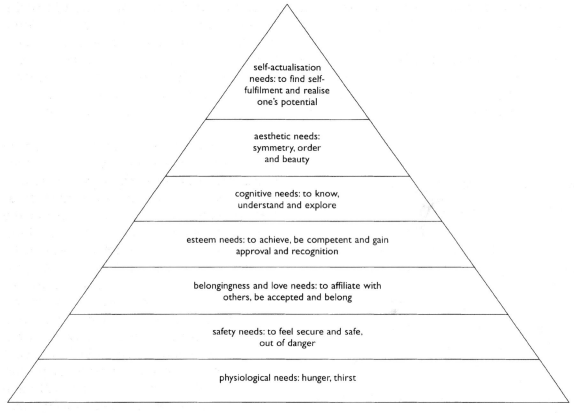

Figure 1.1   Maslow's hierarchy of needs

form, starting with the most basic physio-logical needs at its base and ending with the highest need – for self-actualisation – at its apex.

In Maslow's hierarchy, there are four *deficiency* needs and three *being* needs.

DEFICIENCY NEEDS

- **Physiological needs**: the most basic needs of all human beings are those for food, water, oxygen, elimination, tem-perature regulation, activity, rest and sex; these needs can be closely linked to activities of daily living, such as eating, drinking, eliminating and breathing.
- **Safety and security needs**: protection from potentially dangerous objects or situations, such as the elements or phy-sical illness; psychological need for routine and familiarity.
- **Belongingness and love needs**: receiv-ing and giving love, affection, trust and acceptance; the need for affiliation, being part of a group, whether it be family, friends or work.
- **Esteem needs**: gaining the approval and respect of others; self-esteem and self-respect; the need to achieve and to be competent.

BEING NEEDS

- **Cognitive needs**: exploring, knowing and understanding; the need for mean-ing and predictability.

- **Aesthetic needs**: beauty in art and nature, symmetry, balance, order and form.
- **Self-actualisation needs**: finding self-fulfilment; realising your full potential; it can be summed up in the phrase 'What a person *can* be, he or she ought to be.'

PROGRESSING TO SELF-ACTUALISATION

The highest motive, self-actualisation, involves the emergence of the following qualities:

- toleration of uncertainty
- creativity and an expansion of spiritual and aesthetic experiences
- an appreciation of basic life experiences
- perception of reality
- an acceptance of what our human nature is like, in self and in others
- a concern for humanity.

Self-actualisation is a difficult concept to grasp; it refers to the *potential* within every individual for 'personal growth'. Maslow focused his attention on outstanding people who had demonstrated self-actualisation, for example Albert Einstein, Spinoza and Abraham Lincoln. Some people never fulfil their potential, perhaps because they fail to have a sense of self-worth. In Maslow's terms, they are unable to progress to self-actualisation because their needs for self-esteem have not been met.

Maslow believed that there is an innate tendency to move up the hierarchy of needs in the individual's search for personal fulfilment. The needs at one level must be at least partially satisfied before those at the next level start to motivate behaviour. Maslow understood all these needs to be present simultaneously, but they emerge progressively as they become important and as they are affected by circumstances. For example, if a person is living in an area of famine, then the 'deficiency need' at the base of the pyramid (physiological needs) will assume greater importance. A person who is caught up in a civil war will have the second 'deficiency need' (safety and security needs) as a priority.

Maslow's hierarchy of needs is best seen as a framework of motivation. It is widely used on training courses in business management and health and social care, as it focuses attention on the motives which underlie people's behaviour.

Carl Rogers: self-image and positive regard

Carl Rogers (1902–87) argued that all human beings have two basic needs:

- **The need for self-actualisation**: this may be seen as an active striving for personal development, and manifests itself in perfecting physical skills, educating oneself or realising one's own potential. Rogers believed that all people are born with the actualising tendency. At the lowest level it entails basic needs for physical requirements such as food, water, shelter and comfort. At a higher level it involves the need for self-fulfilment in terms of independence and creativity.
- **The need for positive regard**: healthy personal development occurs through

forming relationships which provide us with affection, love or respect from others. Such positive regard is *unconditional* in that it does not matter how badly we behave, we are still loved just for being ourselves. The individual also needs positive regard from him or herself. Where a person experiences unconditional positive regard, positive self-regard will also be unconditional.

If either of these two basic needs are not met, Rogers argued that psychological problems result. Parents who give love conditionally, perhaps only showing affection when their child is well behaved or fits with their own 'ideal' image, inflict severe psychological damage on the child.

A failure to show unconditional love prevents the child from feeling free to explore his or her own potential and thus achieve self-actualisation. As the child grows to adulthood, he or she will constantly seek approval from others – a classic sign of insecurity. In humanistic terms, the **ideal self** and the **self-concept** are mismatched. Good psychological health exists where the perceived self, or self-concept, and the ideal self are reasonably compatible. Rogers believed that we each need relationships characterised by genuineness, **empathy** and unconditional positive regard and advocated the use of 'encounter groups' in which a trained therapist provides such a relationship in an atmosphere of acceptance and trust.

The inter-relationship of needs

Children's needs may fit into Maslow's and Rogers' frameworks, but self-actualisation is concerned with *mature* development. Mia Kellmer Pringle (1986) states that children have primary and secondary needs. The fulfilment of primary needs – nourishment, shelter and clothing – is necessary for survival. The secondary needs are described as a set of interrelated and interdependent human needs:

- the need for love
- the need for security
- the need for new experience
- the need for praise and recognition
- the need for responsibility.

1 THE NEED FOR LOVE

Children need a stable, continuous, reliable and loving relationship with their parents (or permanent parent-substitutes), who themselves take pleasure from a rewarding relationship with one another. John Bowlby's studies of **attachment** emphasise the importance of the child's need for love and security. His theory of maternal deprivation states that:

- The first five years of life are the most important in a person's development. (This had already been proposed by Freud and other psychodynamic theorists.)
- A child's relationship with his or her parents (in particular with the mother) has an enormous effect on the child's overall development.
- Separation from a parent, particularly from the mother, is a major cause of psychological distress or trauma.
- Such separation and consequent psychological trauma in childhood have

long-lasting effects on the overall development of the child.

- The attachment bond is *monotropic* – this means that it is established between the infant and one other person. Other relationships may be formed, but these differ in quality from the one between the infant and the primary caregiver and do not have the same impact on later social and emotional development.
- Attachment is a highly evolved system of regulation that normally develops during the first year of life to produce a *dynamic equilibrium* between the mother–child pair.
- There exists a *critical (or sensitive) period* for attachment formation. Bowlby thought that the period between six months and three years was critical for attachment formation.
- The basic feature of parental love is that the child is valued unconditionally. The giving of this love does not depend upon any individual differences in appearance or personality. The child is loved for his or her own sake and the love is given without resentment of the demands placed upon the parent.

Michael Rutter (1981) conducted a major review of maternal deprivation research and found – unlike Bowlby – that there is *not* a direct causal link between early experiences of separation from parents and later emotional distress. Rutter believed that:

- A distinction should be made between *disruption* of affectional bonds (where there has been a bond established but that maternal care is lost) and between *privation* of affectional bonds (where children growing up in institutionalised care are denied the opportunity of establishing such bonds).
- A distinction should be made between the *disruption* of affectional bonds (e.g. if

the mother has died) and the *distortion* of relationships within the family, brought about by separation or divorce (when the mother is still physically present).

- The *quality* of family relationships affects the child more than the actual fact of separation or divorce; for example, children separated because of discord between their parents are more likely to show the sort of 'deprivation reaction' which Bowlby described than children separated by the death of a parent.
- The separation of the child from the parents itself is not as significant as the quality of sensitive support given to the child during the experience of separation.
- Multiple attachments can be formed with various people without harm, as long as there is not an extreme form of shared care, e.g. with tens of adults involved.
- Children often appear to be extremely resilient to situations of deprivation; other factors, such as understimulation and minimal social contact, play an unquantifiable part in the overall picture of deprivation.

Bonding

Donald Winnicott (1958), a British psychologist, called the effect of the hormonal changes in late pregnancy 'primary maternal preoccupation'. He described it as a 'state of heightened sensitivity, almost an illness' which made the mother ready to fall in love with her baby – thus creating a mother–infant 'bond'. It used to be thought that this bonding happens rapidly in the first few days (or even hours) after the baby's birth, and that lack of early bonding meant problems in the future. It is now recognised that a bond of attachment is established over a period of time and that it is the *quality* of the time the child spends with people which determines whether or not the child becomes attached to them.

The need to love every child is not an empty sentimental phrase. It means really caring that the child is suffering, even if you don't like him or her much. It also involves not hiding behind the psychology textbook words, such as attachment and bonding, but really listening to the meaning behind words. One extract, reported in *Dagens Nyheter*, a Stockholm newspaper, illustrates the importance of love from the beginning of life:

> The 13th century historian Sallimbeni of Parma, Italy, reports that Emperor Frederik II of the Holy Roman Empire conducted an experiment to find man's original language. He gathered a number of babies and employed wet nurses to care physically for the children, but they were strictly forbidden to talk, cuddle or sing to the babies. By not having any human contact, these children were supposed to develop as naturally as possible. However, all the children died one after another without any apparent reason.

2 THE NEED FOR SECURITY

Children need a secure framework within which to develop. Above all, they need the security of stable family relationships. Children need to be able to rely on the reactions and behaviour of those around them in order to have the confidence to explore the wider world, for example at nursery school or day nursery. They also need the security of a familiar place and known routine. Some children develop a

Figure 1.2   A *transitional object* can be very precious to a child

need for what Winnicott called a *transitional object*. A transitional object may be a cuddly toy, a blanket or a piece of rag to which the baby becomes especially attached. It symbolises the union of the baby and mother at the time they are becoming separate in the baby's mind, and has been described as the 'first not-me possession'.

Such a familiar object gives a feeling of reassurance and security and is often needed at bedtime or in stressful situations. Very young children resist change. They prefer their world to be ordered and predictable. By allowing children to establish rituals and routines that are personal to them, parents and other caregivers acknowledge the child's right to freedom of expression and self-determination.

3 THE NEED FOR NEW EXPERIENCES

Children's learning depends upon their experiences. By presenting children with new experiences and allowing them to build upon previously learned skills, they learn how to make sense of the world – in terms of using their physical abilities, as well as using their growing intellectual abilities and social awareness.

The importance of play

Play is central to a child's learning. It helps children to use what they know and to understand things about the world and the people they meet. From a very early age children learn best by doing, seeing and touching, and they perceive very little difference between work and play. Play is open-ended; even when there is a goal in sight, such as building a tower of blocks, the *process* is more important than the product. Often play is undervalued by adults as taking second place to other aspects of family life. However, if play is to provide a wide range of opportunities for learning, adult involvement is essential.

Jerome Bruner is a psychologist who believes that adults can be a great help to children in their thinking. Bruner's theory of infant skill development has the following features:

- **Enactive thinking**: children need to move about and to have real, first-hand direct experiences; this helps their ideas and thought processes to develop.
- **Iconic thinking**: children need to be reminded of their prior experiences; books and interest tables with objects displayed on them are useful aids to this recall of prior experience.
- **Symbolic thinking**: 'codes' are impor-

Figure 1.3 Examples of symbolic codes: marks made by children of different cultures

tant; languages, music, mathematics, drawing, painting, dance and play are all useful codes which Bruner calls symbolic thinking.
- **Scaffolding**: adults can help develop children's thinking by being like a piece of scaffolding on a building. At first, the building has a great deal of scaffolding (adult support of the child's learning), but gradually, as the children extend their competence and control of the situation, the scaffolding is progressively removed until it is no longer needed.

The use of language

The development of language is closely allied to children's intellectual and conceptual development. It is an important milestone for the developing child as it enables higher levels of communication and provides a channel for expressing emotion and interacting with others. In rare instances where children have been deprived of language, emotional and social development are arrested.

4 THE NEED FOR PRAISE AND RECOGNITION

Children need to have their achievements recognised and praised in order to persevere in their pursuit of knowledge about the world and the people around them. Encouragement and a reasonable level of expectation act as incentives to perseverance. Children who are made to feel like failures when they do not live up to parents' unrealistic expectations become discouraged and make less effort. Children whose parents have too low expectations will similarly adopt a low level of effort and achievement. It is through interaction with others that we gain knowledge of ourselves. Children incorporate the opinions and reactions of others into their self-concept – a process known as *introjection*; this can give rise to a self-fulfilling prophecy. For example:

1 A child who is repeatedly described by his parents as 'very shy' may assimilate this opinion into his self-concept and it then forms part of his *self-attribution*; in other words, he may begin to use 'shy' as a term to describe himself and the shyness may become more pronounced.

2 A nurse in uniform for the first few weeks will adjust his behaviour according to the reactions and expectations of his patients; he may display more self-confidence and higher self-esteem than before wearing the uniform.

3 A student who is told that she will fail

an examination may begin to believe that failure is unavoidable; this may result in her working less hard, failing the exam and thus fulfilling the original prophecy.

Children who are made to feel anxious because of their mistakes often become concerned with avoiding such anxiety. This will hinder the learning process. Praising children when they have tried particularly hard or have achieved something new is an important part in promoting the desire to achieve as an end in itself – a concept called *intrinsic motivation*. Such motivation is often not acquired until adolescence, and even a mature adult will feel encouraged when given some praise or recognition by those whose opinions he or she values.

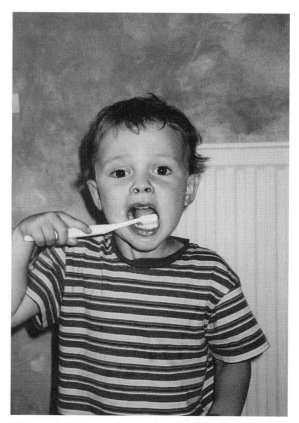

Figure 1.4   Learning to be independent

5 THE NEED FOR RESPONSIBILITY

This need is met by allowing children to gain personal independence. Children learn how to look after themselves in terms of feeding, dressing and washing; see Figure 1.4. Later they are able to exercise freedom of taste in food, play, clothes, choice of friends and hobbies. Adults provide role models for children; what we actually do – or how we behave – influences children's behaviour far more than what we say. Children need a framework of guidance, to know what is acceptable behaviour and what is unacceptable. Schools which emphasise cooperation rather than competition allow their pupils more freedom to accept and exercise responsibility. Children who are involved in the planning of their own activities according to their different interest and ability levels have a greater sense of involvement in the learning process and so feel *empowered* in making decisions which directly affect their lives.

CASE STUDY

Gethin, a three-year-old boy

Gethin is an only child who lives with his young mother, Miriam, in a small flat in an inner-city area. His mother is at her wit's end with the daily effort of coping with Gethin's behaviour. Every weekday, Miriam drops Gethin off at a childminder's house at 8.15 a.m. and goes to the department store where she works as a catering assistant. She picks him up again at 5.45 p.m. and rushes home to prepare the evening meal. Gethin always watches television while she cooks and then they eat their meal together. As soon as he has finished, Gethin starts demanding attention. First he wants a story, then he wants to play a space adventure game, and then he starts throwing his toys around. Miriam often reacts to his demands by shutting him in his room and telling him that he can only come out again when he has learned how to behave. At other times she threatens to cancel the Sunday outings with his father. Weekends are usually taken up with household chores. Gethin's father takes him to the park or to his grandparents' house on Sundays. Gethin loves these visits, but Miriam finds that he demands even more of her attention when he comes home.

activity

1 Examine each of the five needs described on pages 4–9. For each need, list the possible consequences of failure to meet that need, in terms of the effects on the individual. It may be useful to refer to studies of the development of self-concept in a psychology textbook, e.g. *The Science of Mind and Behaviour* by Gross (see bibliography).

2 Read the case study on page 9. Identify any needs which are not being met for Gethin's healthy development. Try to think of ways in which all the needs outlined on pages 4–9 could be met, both for Gethin and for his mother, Miriam.

The need for achievement

Achievement motivation is the tendency to persist at tasks that may be difficult or challenging for the individual. Differences in achievement motivation enable us to explain why less intelligent children may sometimes do better academically than their more intelligent classmates. Research into achievement motivation was pioneered by David McClelland and his colleagues (1953); they saw it as a personality factor responsible for enabling some children to escape the **cycle of disadvantage** which normally operates between home background, education and final occupation. Research has shown that children who have a strong achievement motivation tend to become adults with a strong achievement orientation. The motivation or desire to achieve is influenced by several factors:

- stimulation received from parents during childhood
- the development of a secure attachment relationship
- the development of a clear sense of identity during childhood and adolescence
- acceptance by one's peers, particularly during adolescence
- the ways in which an individual interprets successes and failures, and how they react to challenges; whether they develop a **mastery-oriented** approach or a **learned helplessness** approach to these challenges
- the desire for material rewards
- the feedback obtained from teachers and others
- a belief in the value of hard work – the work ethic.

Special needs

The term special needs is usually applied to those who, generally because of a disability, have needs *additional* to those of others without such a disability. The needs themselves are not different from the basic human needs outlined above, rather, they require help from others to be fulfilled. The term invokes an image in many minds of a person surrounded by elaborate equipment and technology. Paradoxically, an individual is regarded as having special needs when he or she requires help to satisfy one or more of the most basic human needs, that is help with personal care. The term also implies a duty on the relevant organisation to attempt to meet those needs.

If asked to describe their needs, physically disabled people often give a very different picture of their priorities than the professionals who are responsible for deciding on service provision to meet their needs. Special needs for physically disabled people would also include:

- the need for privacy
- freedom to choose, to be independent
- the need for employment.

THE NEED FOR PRIVACY

People who are in residential care often find the lack of privacy at best irksome and, at worst, frustrating and an assault on their dignity. One resident in a home for physically disabled people expresses this frustration:

I feel that I am living independently now in that I can come and go and I can do what I want to do, but I also feel that everyone knows what you are doing. Like if you have a visitor, everybody knows about it.

Although the need for privacy varies from person to person, the less one has of it, the greater is one's need for it. People whose disabilities make their health more vulnerable are possibly likely to have even less privacy. One such affront to a sense of dignity is described by a woman who was not even able to keep the details of her bank account private because the building was inaccessible to wheelchairs. Other comments focus on the inhibiting effect a lack of privacy has on sexual relationships.

FREEDOM TO CHOOSE, TO BE INDEPENDENT

The availability of equipment and adaptations to a home can make a significant impact on the amount of assistance that someone needs and therefore the extent to which they have to rely on a partner or other family member. Also important to the creation of independence is the way in which personal assistance is given. Some people who receive personal assistance from a partner feel a need to maintain some independence within their relationship, while recognising the way that the giving of personal assistance is a positive part of their relationship. Other disabled people find that moving into a residential care establishment actually increases their independence. One disabled woman writes

I first moved into a residential establishment in my 20s and they helped me to get independent. Every few months they had a review of your situation. I liked the freedom that the place gave me. I could see that people wouldn't interfere with what you do, that you could come and go as you wish. I didn't want to be told that I had to be in at half past ten or things like that. Within three years I was engaged to be married and was then offered a bungalow in the grounds of the residential establishment.

Other people complain of the difficulty of moving out once they are in residential care. The main obstacles to moving out are finding suitable housing and, sometimes, the legacy of dependency upon parents.

THE NEED FOR EMPLOYMENT

Disabled people are at a serious disadvantage compared to the rest of the population in the labour market. They are less likely to have paid work: 33 per cent of disabled men and 29 per cent of disabled women are in paid work compared with 78 per cent of men and 60 per cent of women generally. Also, they tend to work on lower-status and lower-paid jobs than their non-disabled counterparts. The effect that this lack of employment has on their lives is obvious: the first consideration is a loss of income; the second is the loss of company and a feeling of dependency.

Assessing needs

In the 1970s, Nancy Roper devised a model for nursing based on 'The activities of daily living'. Drawing on studies in the fields of psychology and sociology, she identified 14 activities essential to life and, more importantly, to the quality of life. Dying is seen as the final activity of living and each activity can be related to two *continua*: The first relates to lifespan (conception–death); the second relates to level of independence (dependence–independence). These aspects provide a useful way of considering how each activity of daily living is influenced by the age and maturity of the person and level of dependence or independence.

The activities of daily living are:

- **Maintaining a safe environment:** comfort, freedom from pain; avoiding injury and infection, monitoring change.

- **Communicating:** verbally and non-verbally; forming relationships; expressing emotions, needs, fears, anxieties; dealing with emotions, positive and negative; maintaining an awareness of the environment; using smell, touch, taste, hearing, seeing and sensitivity.
- **Breathing:** meeting body oxygen needs; maintaining a clear airway and lung expansion.
- **Eating and drinking:** meeting nutritional needs; maintaining a healthy diet, appropriate to the individual; food practicalities: getting food to mouth, chewing, swallowing, appropriate presentation of food; taking in adequate and suitable fluids.
- **Body functions:** passing urine and faeces; maintaining normal and regular functioning and control
- **Personal cleansing and dressing:** skin,

hair, nails, mouth, teeth, eyes, ears; selecting appropriate clothing; dressing and undressing.
- **Maintaing normal body temperature:** physical temperature; adjusting clothing and covers; economic and environmental influences.
- **Mobility:** exercising for health; maintaining muscle tone, circulation; counteracting the effects of immobility, relieving pressure to skin, changing position, aids to mobility.
- **Working and playing:** enjoyment of recreation and pastimes; sense of achievment, independence; partnership in care, rehabilitation.
- **Sexuality:** expressing sexuality, fulfilling needs; reactions to intimate procedures; reproduction.
- **Resting and sleeping:** enjoying a normal sleep pattern; taking rest as desired; a restful environment, without stress, noise.
- **Learning:** discovering, satisfying curiosity; gaining knowledge and skills; awareness of the self as an individual; learning how to care for the self and maintain health; accepting realistic and appropriate goals.
- **Religion:** according to faith and culture; freedom not to worship or believe; movement towards personal spiritual goals, particularly in illness.
- **Dying:** as an inevitability; peacefully, without stress, pain, anxiety; needs met, needs of importance to others met.

Within each activity, the nurse will make an assessment of the person's needs, using the categories as a checklist. Once the patient is assessed by interview, observation and physical examination, a *care plan* is completed.

This model recognises the importance of the influence of external factors:
- **Physical factors:** the person's particular illness or disorder will affect his or her needs.
- **Psychological and emotional factors:** the person's intellectual ability and anxiety or depression will lead to different needs and priorities. For example, severe anxiety may adversely affect all the activities of living, and its alleviation will therefore assume a priority.
- **Sociocultural factors:** the type of family and the relationships within the family will all influence needs. Similarly, the individual's wider community and the social class to which he or she belongs are very influential.
- **Environmental factors:** a person living in a cold, damp house with an outside toilet, for example, will have different needs concerning 'controlling body temperature and eliminating' from someone who is more comfortably housed.
- **Political/economic factors:** poverty or belonging to a disadvantaged group leads to less choice in day-to-day living.

By considering all these factors, we are acknowledging that a person's needs are likely to change according to different circumstances and any assessment of needs must involve this understanding of the wider context in which we all live. Assessment of the individual with special needs is not a once-only event but a *continuous* process. Information gained about the person is added to over a period of time so that a clearer picture is formed of the person's needs. Recognition that these needs may change is an important part of the assessment and review process.

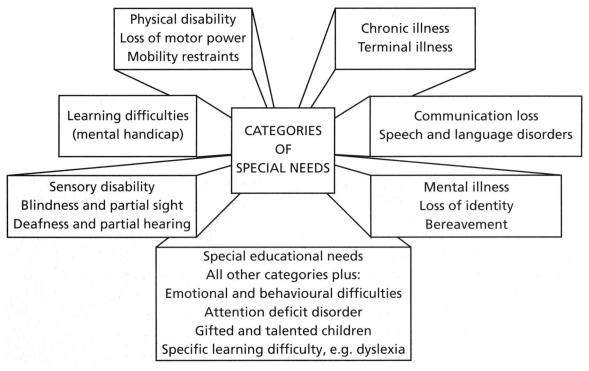

Figure 1.5 Categories of special needs

Intervention

When implementing a care plan, professionals use the following strategies of intervention:

- **Enabling**: this means enabling patients or clients to develop new skills; enabling them to regain their functioning; enabling them to support others.
- **Caring**: this means caring for those who are unable to care for themselves, temporarily or permanently; caring for those who are dying so that they may die with dignity and minimum pain and discomfort.
- **Treatment**: this means treating patients or clients by medication, surgery and/or physiotherapy; and using specialist assessment services such as radiography and physiological measurement.

The planning of patient care follows the medical model of disability (see page 34). It is a very important part of nursing care, which enables the patient to be viewed in a holistic framework. Holistic care involves the treatment of the whole person, and takes into account the social, psychological and environmental influences, including nutrition, exercise and mental relaxation, that affect health. However, for the model to be of maximum benefit to the disabled person, patient participation is encouraged. In situations where the patient is unable or unwilling to participate in the formulation of the care plan, an advocate may be consulted. Advocacy is discussed on page 30.

CHAPTER 2

ATTITUDES AND VALUES OF SOCIETY

The attitudes and values of society are described in this chapter. The possible effects of common perceptions and stereotypes on people with special needs are explained, including social isolation, low self-esteem, embarrassment and difficulty in gaining employment. The concepts of empowerment and advocacy are described, and the ways in which disability may hinder personal development. Models of disability are described in terms of their influence on service provision to those with special needs. A discussion of equality of opportunity, confidentiality issues and types of discrimination in relation to the possible effects on client access to service provision, follows.

In nature there's no blemish but the mind
None can be call'd deformed but the unkind
Twelfth Night, William Shakespeare

How does society view disabled people?

If someone asks you to describe a friend of yours to them, you might do this in a number of ways. For example, you might offer:

- a physical description – colour of skin, eyes, hair; length of hair; size and stature
- a description of their personality – in terms of temperament and personality traits, e.g. cheerful, optimistic, easygoing; anxious, pessimistic, worried
- a description combining physical and personality traits.

If the friend has a particular distinguishing feature, such as red hair, freckles, dreadlocks, a speech stammer or a broad regional accent, you would almost certainly mention that distinguishing feature in your description.

When asked to describe a friend who happens to be disabled in some way, we are very likely to mention the nature of the disability. For example:

- Ian was asked by a colleague what his friend, Tom, was like because the three of them were meeting for a drink after work to arrange a business deal. Tom happens to have athetoid cerebral palsy (see page 61), which causes him to have little control over some physical movements. Ian described Tom thus: 'Tom's got cerebral palsy which makes him pull funny faces sometimes and he walks a bit strangely. But he's a good bloke – you'll like him. He really knows his stuff.'
- Maxine was trying to arrange for someone to keep an eye on her father while she went to visit her daughter in Trinidad. She contacted her local area health authority to enquire about care assistants and nursing aids. When she was connected by phone to the relevant department, she explained that her father had Parkinson's disease (see page 77) and was in need of some sort of surveillance while she was out of the country.

There is nothing wrong with either of the descriptions in the two examples above: they just typify the way in which we like to *categorise* people, to define them in simple, everyday terms that other people can understand. Ian may have felt embarrassed for his friend Tom. He probably wanted to avoid any awkward reaction from his colleague. Maxine needed to get information from the health and social care staff about what was available for her father; by describing him in terms of his disability (Parkinson's disease), she knew that the care personnel would be aware of the sort of problems they would meet and what kind of help might be necessary.

Assumptions about disabled people

People behave differently towards disabled people. People who are nondisabled make certain assumptions about physically disabled people. Some assumptions are that:

- they desperately want to be normal
- they feel that they are a burden to others
- they are envious of able-bodied people
- they should put up with inconvenience and discomfort to take part in 'normal' activities
- they feel ugly and unwanted
- they are angry and frustrated, and can never really accept their disability

- friends or partners stick by them out of duty or charity
- an acquired disability is all the more tragic if the person was previously gifted, successful or attractive
- if they appear happy, they are merely putting on a brave face
- any emotion they show is due to their disability and not due to the same causes that affect non-disabled people
- if they are not in a long-term relationship or married, then it must be because nobody wants them
- when they say they don't want to do something, it is usually because they don't want to be a nuisance to others

- Saying 'see you soon' to a blind person, or 'I'm going for a walk' to a person in a wheelchair will upset them
- they are somehow 'ennobled' by having a disability; they are sweet, deprived souls who need to be praised for every achievement.

Wolfensberger (1975) lists eight *social role perceptions* of people with learning difficulties which have implications for the way in which this group of people is treated by the rest of society. They are seen as:

- subhuman
- sick
- an eternal child
- holy innocents (being regarded as without original sin)
- an object of pity, and a burden of charity
- an object of ridicule
- a menace
- an object of dread.

The following poem sums up some common assumptions made about disabled people:

Do Unto Others

I was waiting at the checkout and leaning on my crutch
When a voice behind me loudly said, 'Come, come, this is too much!'

'Hey, Miss,' she called. 'Young lady! I say! Now listen, dear,
You'd better get a move on, we've got a cripple here!'

The cashier's tapping fingers stopped, she looked around to see
Who this pathetic creature was – I realised it was *me* . . .

'Now let me help unpack your load – the least that I can do –
Because, but for the grace of God, I could be just like you!

'Does anybody help you? Or do you live alone?
Oh, do you buy this in a tin? I always bake my own.

'You haven't got a husband? Well, build a social life –
Perhaps you'll meet a crippled man who wants a crippled wife!'

I found this quite offensive, and told her so, at length
She said, 'My dear, I understand – you've lost your health and strength.

'I know you're being very brave, but that *was* rather rude –
Next time someone helps you, try to show some gratitude.

Of course you think life isn't fair, but when you're feeling blue –
Big smile! And then remember, there's someone worse than you!'

Janice Pink
(taken from *Mustn't Grumble*, edited by Lois Keith)

activity

Read the poem on page 17 and then list the assumptions made about the writer.

Marginalisation

Marginalisation is the process by which certain individuals or groups are pushed to the periphery of, and sometimes excluded from, mainstream society. Disabled people are at risk of marginalisation and have long been perceived as having negative status. In the past, attitudes towards disability have been determined by notions of what is normal and by the idea that people who deviate from this norm should be segregated, as much for their own benefit as for that of the 'normal' population. In ancient Greece, disabled infants were killed at birth; this was partly because any deviation from the norm was seen as punishment meted out by the gods, and partly because disabled children would become an economic burden on their family.

In the eighteenth century there was a successful move among the deaf community to promote communication by signing (see page 152). However, this move was suppressed by the wider community, possibly because of the widely held belief that all disability should be eradicated and that encouraging deafness would lead to more people becoming deaf. Even now, in spite of professional support for signing as a means of communication, there are many who feel that deaf people should learn to use oral language (i.e. to speak) in order to fit in with the rest of society.

Finkelstein (1980) sees the marginalisation of disabled people partly as a consequence of the industrial revolution. In the days of cottage industries, where people worked from home, those who deviated from the norm because of disability were still capable of earning a living. As more machinery was introduced into the manufacturing process, physically and mentally disabled people were excluded from the workplace. Potential workers in the machine-run factories not only had to be 'able-bodied' but also had to be able to follow instructions designed for 'normal' workers, that is oral and sometimes complicated written instructions. In this way, people classed as 'cripples' or 'mental defectives' were reduced to begging or to relying on charitable hand-outs. They were thus marginalised and prevented from participating in the creation of social wealth.

Defining terms

The language used to describe disability and disabled people is highly charged and constantly changing. What suits one person doesn't suit another.

HANDICAP

Many disabled people find the word 'handicapped' offensive, as it carries connotations of being dependent on charity and a patronising attitude. (The term originates from the notion of 'hand in the cap', i.e. begging for money or charity.) Charities such as Mencap now prefer the use of the words 'learning disabilities', but other organisations prefer 'learning difficulties'.

IMPAIRMENT AND DISABILITY

Impairment refers to the functional limitations which affect a person's body. Disability refers to the loss or limitation of opportunities owing to social, physical and attitudinal barriers. Jenny Morris, a disabled writer, defines them as follows:

- An inability to walk is an impairment.
- An inability to enter a building because the entrance is up a flight of steps is a disability.
- An inability to speak is an impairment.
- An inability to communicate because appropriate technical aids are not made available is a disability.
- An inability to move one's body is an impairment.
- An inability to get out of bed because appropriate help is not available is a disability.

A definition of disability offered by Disabled People's International is: 'the loss or limitation of opportunities to take part in the normal life of the community on an equal level with others due to physical and social barriers.' People are disabled by society's reaction to impairments. This is why the term 'disabled people' is often used, rather than 'people with disabilities'. However, some disabled people believe that the correct term is 'person with a disability', because an individual is a person first. The word 'disabled' should not be used as a collective noun, i.e. 'the disabled'; use of a collective noun implies that disabled people are a homogeneous group, separate from the rest of society. Similarly, 'the handicapped' should never be used, for this reason and for the connotations mentioned above.

Do not say
- the mentally handicapped; subnormal or retarded
- victim of; crippled by; suffering from; afflicted by
- wheelchair bound or confined to a wheelchair
- he/she is a spastic; he/she is an epileptic
- 'invalid': this equates disability with illness (see medical model on page 34); it also has a double 'literal' meaning, i.e. not valid
- normal
- handicap; disease; affliction; illness.

Do say
- people with learning difficulties
- person who has; person who experienced; person with

- wheelchair user, or person who uses a wheelchair
- he/she has cerebral palsy; he/she is a person with epilepsy

- non-disabled; able-bodied
- disabling condition
- impairment.

Image and self-concept

Disability has been described as a very ordinary part of life. It is the commonly accepted myths and stereotypes about disabled people, frequently reinforced by the media, which make disability seem an extraordinary and abnormal thing. The standard image of the slim, youthful, 'perfect' physique can seriously damage a disabled person's **self-esteem**.

Self-esteem is closely associated with **self-concept**. Margaret Donaldson, a psychologist with a particular interest in the development of children's minds, argues that children can only develop a strong self-concept when they feel they are effective, competent and independent. A child with special needs may have weaknesses in these areas and this may result in a lowering of self-esteem. Within the confines of the family environment, the child will probably have a positive self-image, as she has been encouraged in her all-round development to use the skills she possesses. When the child starts playgroup, nursery or school, she will come into contact with other children and adults who are not necessarily as supportive as her parents. She may find that she is stared at, or that people avoid her, or she may be asked lots of questions about her difficulties. Other factors which can affect the child's self-concept include:

- **Comparisons with other children**: it is a natural part of development for children to judge their own abilities and strengths in comparison with their peers.
- **The need to fulfil untypical childhood roles**: a child with special needs may have to adapt to a role not normally associated with childhood, for example the role of 'someone who needs extra help with reading', or 'someone who sits out of PE classes', or 'someone who needs a wheelchair'.
- **Physical appearance**: children with special needs have the same system of values about attractiveness and physical appearance as do all children. If asked to draw a self-portrait, a child with a physical disability may draw a picture:
  - in which the disability is completely *ignored*; in other words she draws herself without the disability
  - in which the disability is *hidden*; for example the child may draw herself behind a wall so that only her head shows
  - in which the disability is *exaggerated*; for example her wheelchair may be disproportionately large; see Figure 2.1.
- **Identification**: feelings of self-esteem are influenced by the process of identifying with, firstly, her parents and later with other adults and friends; parental attitudes about the way the child's difficulties are managed directly affect the child's self-concept.
- **The self-fulfilling prophecy**: our expectations of people's personalities or skills

Figure 2.1 How a physically disabled 8-year-old drew himself

may influence the way that we actually treat them; this in turn may influence their behaviour in such a way that our expectation is confirmed. A teacher who always asks for a 'nice, strong boy' to help her clear away large equipment, and for a 'nice, quiet girl' to collect the register is not only reinforcing gender stereotypes; the girl may believe that only boys are strong and this belief will influence the way she behaves. Children with special needs are best served by people having higher expectations in all areas of development; this approach, combined with a realistic appraisal of their capabilities, will help children towards independence and an improved self-concept.

Of all the media, television is the most powerful reinforcer of the image that society is a place for and peopled by ideal human beings – the healthy, the attractive and the 'normal'.

The Royal Association of Disability and Rehabilitation (RADAR) has drawn up a code of practice to guide those involved in the press, radio and television. The code of practice is designed to focus the attention of journalists, programme producers and others away from seeing 'the disabled' as a special group, and towards seeing everyone in society as an individual. Many people, says RADAR, simply regard the difficulties associated with their disabilities as a normal part of life. To describe them as 'sufferers' is both inaccurate and patronising. Other descriptions which are often used in the media, but which should be avoided are 'crippled by', 'a victim of' or 'afflicted by' a disability. The phrase 'confined to a wheelchair' should be replaced with 'wheelchair user', as from the point of view of the user the wheelchair is an aid to mobility and not a restriction. Far from imprisoning and restricting the user, a wheelchair sets the user free in terms of mobility. Disabled children are constantly exposed to images that show disabled people as unwanted burdens or disappointments to their parents. The drive by professionals to make the child achieve 'normal' milestones, such as walking and talking, can make failure – if and when it happens – even more tragic. The child may feel second best to all those children who do manage to walk and talk at the prescribed times; in this way, and in countless others, their self-esteem is irrevocably harmed.

activity

1 What's in a name?

Discuss the language used to describe disability: 'differently abled'; 'physically challenged'; 'the handicapped'; 'mentally retarded'; educationally subnormal'; etc. Think of the words you have heard or used to describe disabled people.

- Do you think that the use of a certain terminology is important? If so, why?
- Which descriptions do you think disabled people would feel good about, and which would damage their self-esteem?

2 Disabled images in the media

This task should be carried out over a three-week period.

Divide into three groups. Each group should sample a different branch of the media for three hours every weekday evening between 7.30 and 10.30 p.m.

Group A BBC Radio 2 and 4, Talk Radio UK

Group B TV BBC 1 and BBC 2, ITV or Channel 4

Group C Newspapers: Two broadsheet papers, e.g. the *Guardian*, *The Times*, the *Independent*, the *Daily Telegraph*; and two tabloid papers, e.g. the *Daily Mail*, the *Sun*, the *Daily Express*, the *Mirror*.

Each group should change weekly so that they have each sampled the three media areas outlined above. Prepare a report detailing the nature of the programmes and articles. In particular, answer the following questions:

1 Were disabled people represented in the media?
2 If disabled people were represented, how were they portrayed and what language was used to describe them or their disabilities?
3 Were any stereotypes used?

At the end of the three-week period, each group should prepare a five-minute presentation for the rest of the class, illustrating their findings.

Adjustment to disability

Whether people are suddenly disabled, as in a road traffic accident (RTA), or gradually, as with the slow deterioration of multiple sclerosis, a variety of psychological factors are involved. Because a *loss* has occurred, all disabled people may experi-ence grief, denial, depression and a struggle for reintegration. Although needs are specific to the individual person concerned, there are areas in which health and social care workers could intervene to make adjustment easier.

1 ENCOURAGE THE DISABLED PERSON TO EXPRESS FEELINGS

It is important that carers ask questions (e.g. Can you help me understand what you are feeling?) that give the person permission to talk about those feelings. Relatives and close friends of the disabled person will need to be able to express their feelings too, as they may also be experiencing loss.

2 DO NOT MAKE PROMISES OR GIVE FALSE REASSURANCE

Caregivers should not communicate false reassurance about recovery. The goal for both the disabled person and the caregiver should be to find ways for them to live with the disability while achieving as normal a life as possible. This is best achieved by empowering the disabled person to the goal of independence and autonomy.

3 COMMUNICATE EMPATHY

Empathy, or the sharing of another's emotions and feelings, is an important aspect of any caring relationship. Being able to understand another's feelings, even when we have not had similar life experiences, helps us to assess their needs and to work with them to meet these. Empathy should not be confused with sympathy. A carer acting out of a sense of sympathy may take over some tasks for a disabled person, when the best course would be to enable the person to achieve personal independence.

4 ENCOURAGE A POSITIVE SELF-CONCEPT

Self-concept is closely associated with body image, self-esteem and identity. Any loss of or alteration in any of these factors can cause problems of acceptance and adjustment. This is best achieved by increasing the activities they can do well and reducing the number that they do poorly, but the methods of helping are as diverse as the individuals involved.

5 BE AWARE OF CULTURAL DIFFERENCES

Individual needs will differ according to their cultural and ethnic background. For example, among Greek Cypriots there is usually a period of weeping and wailing after the death of a loved one; this is followed by a defined period of mourning and wearing black. The Irish wake involves watching of the corpse by relatives for several days and nights, and sometimes involves feasting and drinking.

6 BUILD A NETWORK OF SUPPORT

This network of support may include family members in the home, extended family and professionals. Children need specialised support when a parent becomes disabled, because the shift in focus to the disabled person often leads to neglect of the needs of the children. Parents and siblings also need help with adjustment when a child in their family has a chronic illness or is otherwise disabled.

7 GUIDE TOWARDS SEEKING EMPLOYMENT

Unemployment contributes to the physical and psychological distress of disabled people; finding employment or substitute activities can play a key role in maintaining a positive mental state. It is important that they are not placed in a vocational setting restricted to disabled people, because such settings may enhance feelings of *disempowerment*.

8 CULTIVATE A POSITIVE AND REALISTIC OUTLOOK ON LIFE

Disabled people need to recognise their personal areas of strength and control and to capitalise on them. Johnny Creschendo, a singer with disabilities, sums it up:

> My body's got self-dignity
> My body's got self-respect
> No-one can take that away from me
> In this world or the next.
>
> Creschendo, 1989

Learned helplessness

People with disabilities often feel disempowered, which leads to feelings of helplessness, summed up as, 'It doesn't matter what I do or say – nothing makes any difference to what will happen to me.' The concept of learned helplessness can be seen as a passive condition where the individual has learned, from prior experience, that they have no control over their own fate and so there is no point in making any effort to better the situation. Martin Seligman (1975) proposed that a lot of depression in adults and elderly people was a result of learned helplessness. A disabled person who is denied the right to choose how to live, because he or she is dependent on others for personal care, may find it less of a daily struggle to leave decisions and even manageable aspects of care to others. This then sets up a 'vicious circle': as the person becomes disempowered, others take control of his or her daily living needs. The person then opts out of any active involvement in decision-making and personal care. Frustration and anger at this state of affairs gives way to withdrawal from society and depression.

Discrimination

Discrimination is the unfair treatment of a person or a group, usually because of a negative view of certain of their characteristics. Having a physical disability means living in society as part of a *minority group* whose particular needs are not adequately recognised or taken into account, and whose different appearance often leads to its members being treated differently and less equally. Of course, not all disabilities are readily recognisable as such; for example, deafness, diabetes and epilepsy are not immediately obvious.

The following are all attitudes commonly encountered by disabled people from non-disabled people:

- **Stereotyping**: one example is the logo denoting access for disabled people; the sign shows a person in a wheelchair, yet less than 5 per cent of the 6 million people with disabilities in the UK use wheelchairs.
- **Dependency**: one example of the assumption that disabled people are dependent is the 'kind' individual who firmly guides a blind person across the road when they were merely waiting for a friend to come out of a nearby shop.
- **Hostility**: this may take the form of loud comments being made about the disabled person, or aggression. For example, one disabled woman writes: 'I went to the Ideal Home Exhibition, and this horrible woman with a dog crashed into my chair and she said, "You shouldn't be allowed in here." My friend said, "You shouldn't be allowed in here with your silly little dog." People can be rude sometimes.'
- **Exclusion**: physical or intellectual differences can make disabled people less than human in the eyes of non-disabled people; so it follows that they can be excluded from normal human activity because they are 'not normally human'. Disabled people are often excluded from social events because they are held in areas which are inaccessible to wheelchair users.
- **Invasion of privacy**: the attitudes of others to those with a disability which is highly visible is often one of well-intentioned over-friendliness, or worse, expressions of revulsion. Somehow, a disabled person is thought to have less ownership of his or her body and personal space than a non-disabled person. Curiosity about the nature of the dis-

Figure 2.2 The patronising attitude towards disability

ability can lead to intrusive questions being asked about very private aspects of daily life.

- **Patronage**: a patronising attitude again underlies an assumption of dependency on the part of the disabled person, for example the humiliation of people talking to the wheelchair user's non-disabled companion as if the disabled person would not be able to understand or to answer what is being said.

STEREOTYPING

Stereotyping is the process whereby groups or individuals are characterised in simplified and often negative and unflattering terms, so that all members of the category are seen in one particular way. A stereotype is:

- a way of classifying and categorising other people who are different from us
- an assumption based on opinion rather than fact

- a general picture, without any details
- often a way of saying that we are superior to others
- often applied to a variety of groups – racial, national, age, gender, etc.
- a way of lumping everyone in a group together as having the same characteristics
- a way of leading us to believe that we know how others will behave.

Here are some examples of stereotypes:

- British youths on holiday are only interested in sex and getting drunk.
- Teenage girls are always on a diet.
- All young people from the Netherlands are high on drugs most of the time.
- Football fans are noisy, loud-mouthed and looking for a fight.
- Children with Down's syndrome are always cheerful.

activity

Individually, list the common stereotypes that are used to classify the following groups of people:

- deaf people
- blind people
- gay people (male and female)
- drug addicts
- mentally disabled people
- people in wheelchairs
- elderly people
- college students.

In a group, compare your lists with each other and note how many similarities there are.

EXCLUSION

Exclusion from any aspect of care is a form of discrimination. Unfortunately, many disabled people do experience exclusion from different aspects of medical and social care. One such exclusion is described in the account which follows:

CASE STUDY

Exclusion from medical care

Many stories of discrimination are difficult to prove. It is the individual, not the sex, category or the colour of the skin of those discriminated against that is the problem. But for Joanne Harris, and the hundreds of children with Down's syndrome like her, there is no such evasion. Joanne is dying. Every day she becomes a little weaker, more breathless. Joanne is 13 years old and has a hole in her heart. Doctors have said that she will not live for long in her present state, and that by the time she is 18 she will almost certainly be in a wheelchair. Joanne desperately needs a heart and lung transplant.

Joanne attends a comprehensive school in Shrewsbury, and in the ugly medical jargon, is termed a 'high-grade' Down's syndrome child. She is taught in a special unit with a number of other children with learning difficulties. She likes swimming, boys and pop music. She loves – and is loved by – her mother, Marion and father Mike, her brother Craig and two sisters, Helen and Katie. If Joanne had been born within the last few years she would have stood some chance of having corrective heart surgery (as Hannah did – see page 102), but when she was born, 'normal' children took priority over those with Down's syndrome.

Until recently, British transplant teams were able to defend their policy of excluding patients with Down's syndrome on medical grounds. People with Down's syndrome, they argued, often have a lowered immune system and are more susceptible to colds and flu. This led the teams to believe that the valuable donor organs might be wasted on patients who would pick up an infection post-operatively and die. Now, however, a transplant immunologist has stated that this lowered immune system, far from jeopardising recovery, actually aids the process. Another argument used in the exclusion of patients with Down's syndrome was that because of their learning difficulties, they would be unlikely to work closely with the transplant team in taking their drugs and cooperating with what were frequently painful medical procedures. This argument of *compliance* is obviously flawed in that transplants are often carried out on infants, who are in no position to consent or comply with anything.

In the USA, there are strong anti-discrimination laws to protect the rights of disabled people. In January 1996, Sandra Jensen was the first person with Down's syndrome in the world to receive a heart and lung transplant. The mother of the 35-year-old patient describes the attempts by doctors to intimidate her daughter into refusing the operation.

> One doctor asked Sandra why she wanted the operation. When she said, 'Because I want to live', he said, 'That is not a good enough reason.' I thought, 'If wanting to live is not a good enough reason, then what is?'

The doctors refused to accept that Sandra had the capability to make up her own mind. Sandra said:

> They kept saying to me, 'You don't really want this operation.' I had to tell them a hundred times that I did. They were trying to make a decision for me. I knew I had to fight hard because I wanted to be healthy, not sick all the time. I know I'm retarded. I know that can't be fixed. But if I could change myself ... I wish I could be reborn. I don't want to be slow anymore. I want to be fast. Sometimes I have dreams about it. I dream things like being able to tap dance, or do a little ballet. But then I wake up. And it's the same. I walk slow. I talk slow. My mind moves too slow. And sometimes that's harder than anybody understands. But I don't want to die.

Sandra received the transplant within one week of being accepted on to the waiting list, and so far has confounded the medical critics by being healthy long after the one-third of all patients who die within months

contd. ⓘ▮▮▮➡

▐▐▐➡

of the operation. Sandra's employer, who campaigned for treatment on her behalf, sees Sandra Jensen's case as the first battle in a long war for disabled entitlement.

A lot of doctors still suffer from the old mentality. They define people with disabilities as people with a chronic, terminal, treatmentless condition. They don't see people with disabilities as we see them – as sons and daughters, family members, community members and part of the richness of everyday life. For them, this is a disease category that is sort of hopeless. So the idea of giving away a quarter-of-a-million-dollar set of organs, you know, to somebody that's a labelled person is anathema.

For the Harris family, the discrimination endured by Joanne is all too real.

Jo hasn't been given a chance. It makes me so angry. Joanne's not a priority because she has learning difficulties. She's a priority to us, she's our daughter ... Some human lives will never travel far, but that does not diminish their worth. A life like Jo's is as full of joy, struggle, pain and human endeavour as any other. A heart and lung transplant may or may not be the right thing for her. That is a judgement to be made by transplant specialists on medical grounds alone. But as a society, in having a heart for Jo, in understanding and embracing human diversity, and according her the same rights as all others, we can at least affirm our own imperfect humanity.

activity

The rationing of health and social care

There are many different ways in which health care is rationed. Demand for services will always exceed supply. Working individually, rank the following main areas of health and social care in order of importance:

- preventative services (e.g. screening, immunisations)
- medical research for new treatments
- treatments for children with life-threatening illnesses (e.g. leukaemia)
- transplants which treat life-threatening conditions (e.g. heart, lung or kidney transplants)

- special care and pain relief for people who are dying (e.g. hospice care)
- intensive neonatal care for pre-term babies who weigh less than one and a half pounds and are unlikely to survive.
- surgery (e.g. hip replacement) to help disabled people perform everyday tasks
- community services/care at home (e.g. district nurses)
- therapy to help disabled people perform everyday tasks (e.g. physiotherapy, speech and occupational therapy)
- services for mentally ill people (e.g. psychiatric wards, community psychiatric nurses)

- treatments for infertility (e.g. test tube babies)
- long stay residential care (e.g. hospital and nursing homes for elderly people).

Compare your list with a friend's and discuss any differences between them.

activity

This activity involves an investigation of discrimination against disabled people: its nature and its effects, and possible ways of preventing it. In particular you will need to find out about:

- the different forms which discrimination may take
- the ways in which people are affected by the experience of discrimination.

Stage 1

As a whole group, and with the help of your teacher, research and discuss ideas for designing, carrying out and analysing a survey into people's attitudes towards and experiences of discrimination and disability. You will be expected to work constructively within the group, participating in discussion and suggesting ideas.

Stage 2

(a) In small groups, write down ideas for questions to ask as part of this survey. These questions will then be collated into a **pilot study**.
(b) As a whole group, share the task of piloting the survey and redesigning questions where necessary. Produce a final version of this survey.

Stage 3

(a) As a whole group, share the task of administering the survey to the sample decided upon.
(b) Play an active part in designing and using an observation sheet to collect the data generated by the survey. Within the whole group, collate and present the results of the survey as a wall display, using different methods of representation such as tables, pie charts, graphs and scales.

Stage 4

Complete, individually, a written report (using guidelines set by your teacher or set out below) which:

- analyses and interprets the results of the whole group survey
- suggests ways in which discrimination against disabled people may be prevented.

Stage 5

(a) Interview in depth – on audio-tape or on video – three separate individuals of different ages concerning their views on or experiences of discrimination (or both) relating to:

  - gender
  - age
  - race

  or a combination of two or more of these factors.
(b) Write a summary of these interviews (including the questions you asked). Compare the views and experiences you found out about.
(c) Prepare a short (3–5 minutes) video

presentation of this summary, briefly describing the interviews and what you learned from them. This video will be shown to the rest of the group.

Stage 6

Individually, complete an evaluation sheet to say how the investigation went, how each member of the group (including yourself) contributed to the tasks and what you learned.

Guidelines for a written report on the survey investigating people's attitudes towards and experiences of discrimination and disability

1 Why did you carry out this survey? What were you looking for? To answer these questions, look at the questions you asked in the survey. What did you want to know?

2 How did you carry out this survey? What methods did you use? To answer these questions, explain exactly how you did the survey. How did you decide on the questions? What was the pilot study for? How many people did you ask, and why? Did you ask people to fill in the questionnaires, or did you do it for them? Did you have different types of questions? If so, why?

3 What did the results of the survey show? To answer this question, explain each of them using the display of graphs and tables or your copies of these, or both. Write a summary of the results of each question in the survey. Say what the results show and what they might imply about disability and discrimination. Try to explain this and account for each of the results.

4 If you had a chance to do a survey like this again, how would you improve it? To answer this, say what you think you could have done to improve this survey. Could you have improved the methods you used or the questions you asked? If so, how? What could have been done better, or differently? Could you have made more use of the results in any way? Did you actually find any useful or interesting information? Try to think of at least three ways in which the survey could have been improved, and explain each one fully.

5 Does the survey give you ideas about how discrimination against disabled people might be prevented? Explain these ideas.

Advocacy

Advocacy has variously been defined as 'pleading the cause of another' or 'a means of transferring power back to the patient, to enable them to control their own affairs'. Advocacy is a means of helping people to secure their rights and to get the services they both want and need. It has become widely accepted by health and social care services and by voluntary organisations. Advocacy aims to empower service users, not to let others take over. An advocate is someone independent from these services who befriends an individual service user, on a one-to-one basis, and represents their interest to professionals. Therefore it is vital that a relationship of trust is established between the person, his or her family and the advocate. Sometimes relatives and friends are able to act as advocates, provided that there is no conflict of interest. Recently, there has been a growth of formal advocacy schemes, which are grouped into one of the following categories:

- **Professional advocacy**: support is provided by a paid advocate, with training and support from an organisation which is independent of those who are providing services to the user.
- **Citizen advocacy**: the user is helped and supported by an unpaid volunteer, usually a person who is trained and supported, in turn, by a voluntary organisation.
- **Self-advocacy**: the user represents him or herself, supported by a group of fellow service users.
- **Legal advocacy**: the user is represented by a solicitor or law centre who may be involved in court proceedings or at a health or social care review tribunal.

The areas in which advocacy is most needed and most used are those of mental illness and severe learning difficulties. Advocacy is seen as ever more vital with the closure of large psychiatric hospitals and the increase in community care.

The movement for *child advocacy* began in the USA in the 1960s. In the UK, the Children Act 1989 makes social services departments responsible for providing for children with special needs; 'A child is disabled if he is blind, deaf, or dumb or suffers from mental disorder of any kind or is substantially and permanently handicapped by illness, injury or congenital deformity or other such disability as may be described.' The concept of advocacy is enshrined in the Act. It recognises that disabled children are least likely to be able to speak up for themselves – that is, to recognise their own needs and to know how to achieve them. Therefore, they need an advocate. Usually the advocate is an adult care worker who acts as a *spokesperson* for the person 'in need'.

Empowerment

This concept is closely linked to advocacy. It involves the process of making someone feel more powerful. To empower someone is to enable them to:

- control their own lives
- make their own decisions
- achieve positive self-esteem
- acquire a strong sense of identity.

Advocacy is one means of empowerment. Empowerment may also be achieved by disabled people through self-directed group work, where people with similar needs decide on their own goals using the help of professionals if required. In this way, awareness is raised through cooperative effort and it avoids the assumption that the answer to problems lies only with the individual.

The British Council of Organisations of Disabled People (BCODP) was formed in the 1980s to develop *self-empowerment* among groups of disabled people. In this context, self-empowerment is seen as disabled people taking a more important role in policy-making.

Autonomy and independence

Autonomy means, literally, self-rule and refers to the extent to which an individual can think, decide and act independently. Closely linked to autonomy is the concept of independence, the idea that we are most fully human when we can decide for ourselves what we want and can achieve it without dependence on others. Independence is the freedom to do something. In some affluent countries, notably in Scandinavia, Canada and the USA, measures have been taken to increase autonomy and independence by, for instance, adapting housing and paying allowances directly to disabled people to spend on services as they wish, rather than leaving decisions to professionals. This goes a long way to increasing self-empowerment.

LANGER AND RODIN'S STUDY

Langer and Rodin (1976) noted that declining physical skills and a lowered sense of usefulness can create in elderly people a feeling of lack of control over their fate, similar to the concept of learned helplessness (see page 24); the generally negative attitudes towards elderly people in this society further increase their dependency or lack of autonomy.

In their study, Langer and Rodin attempted to assess the effects of enhanced personal responsibility and choice in a group of patients in a nursing home.

The method

They selected two groups on separate floors of the large nursing home who were matched for similar health and socio-economic status; each group was given a talk by the nursing home administrator, which he introduced as some information about the home.

The experimental group
The main points of the talk were:

- You have the responsibility of caring for yourselves.
- You can decide how you would like your rooms arranged.
- You can decide how you wish to spend your time.
- It's your life.
- It's your responsibility to make complaints known.

They were also offered a plant as a present, told that there was a movie showing in the home on Thursday and Friday, and asked which night, if any, they would like to go.

The control group
A similar talk was given but with important differences:

- There was no emphasis on personal responsibility.
- They were not encouraged to take control in the nursing home.
- They were *given* the present of a plant rather than offered it, and told that they were scheduled to see the movie one night or the other, and told how the staff tried to make their rooms nice.

Questionnaires and interviews were used to assess the sense of control, happiness and level of activity each group had both one week after the talk and three weeks later. The research assistant and the nurses were unaware of the hypothesis and the methods of the experiment.

The results

Substantial differences between the two groups were reported by the patients, the interviewer ratings and the nurse ratings. The people in the experimental group were found to be happier, more active, more alert and generally much more socially active than the control group; they also spent less time watching the staff.

The researchers went back to the home after 18 months and found that the people in the experimental group were *still* improved in comparison to the control group; also they were in better health and fewer had died. It was concluded that a relatively minor intervention had achieved a remarkable effect on the health and well-being of the residents in the nursing home.

INDEPENDENT LIVING

In the UK, the legal status of disabled people is still primitive, whereas in the USA, Bill Clinton's administration has established a special Washington unit dedicated to disability with a staff of 414 and a budget of $5.3 billion (£3.5 billion). The head of the unit is herself a wheelchair user and believes that disabled people now enjoy considerable political leverage on Congress Hill.

The general movement by people with disabilities towards greater *integration* into mainstream society and greater *control* over their own futures has become embodied in the *Independent Living Movement*. The philosophy of the movement is based on four assumptions:

- that all human life is of value
- that anyone, whatever their impairment, is capable of exerting choices
- that people who are disabled by society's reaction to physical, intellectual and sensory impairment and to emotional distress have the right to assert control over their lives
- that disabled people have the right to participate fully in society.

The concept of independent living is a broad one, involving human and civil rights. Having control over their lives does not mean that disabled people have to be able to care for themselves without assistance. Independence is created by having control over the personal assistance that is required to go about daily life, by deciding when and how one requires it.

THE MEANING OF CARE WHEN RELATED TO PERSONAL INDEPENDENCE

Jenny Morris (1993), questions the use of the terms 'carers', 'caring' and 'dependent people'. She writes:

> Those who need help with daily living activities cannot be treated with respect, their autonomy cannot be promoted, if their physical requirements are assumed to turn them into 'dependent people'. Neither can their personal relationships be respected if their partner, parent or relative is treated as a 'carer'. We need to reclaim the words 'care' and 'caring' to mean 'love', to mean 'caring *about*' someone rather than 'caring *for*', with its custodial overtones.

She also argues that:

> While impairment is seen as necessarily creating dependency, as being a problem, a welfare issue for society to deal with, policies will always be at variance

with disabled people's civil rights. Impairment and old age need to be seen as part of our (i.e. the whole society's) common experience.

Models of special needs

The development of models arose from the need to give a structure or framework to the provision of services for disabled people. Formal models are those which aim to determine the provision in its broadest sense, that is:

- which organisations will provide services
- how the provision of services is regulated and funded
- which professionals in health, education and social care are involved.

They look at *groups* of people with special needs and how they can best be served.

THE WORLD HEALTH ORGANISATION (WHO) MODEL

A national survey was conducted by the Office of Population Censuses and Surveys (OPCS). Published in 1971, it arrived at a threefold classification of disability:

- **impairment** – lacking all or part of a limb, or having a defective limb, organ or mechanism of the body (i.e. a part of the body does not work properly or is missing)
- **disability** – the loss or reduction of functional ability (i.e. what people cannot do when compared with the majority of other people)
- **handicap** – the disadvantage or restriction of activity caused by disability (i.e.

what an individual can and cannot do in a particular situation, and in relationships with other people).

This 'welfare' model of disability shaped the provision of services and benefits. Services are offered by the 'able-bodied' world to compensate the disabled person for the difficulties of living with disability. Services and welfare benefits are still under the control of health and social welfare agencies, which assess disabled people and decide who should have access to which services and benefits. In this way, it is closely linked to the medical model of disability.

THE MEDICAL MODEL

In the medical model, disabled people are often 'lumped together' as a unified group, dependent on medical practitioners to define their needs. They represent a *problem* for the medical profession; they need monitoring and solutions have to be found. This approach to disability has rightly been criticised as having a *negative* focus; it does not highlight the abilities and needs that disabled people have in common with everyone else. Disabled people are defined largely by the medical causes and effects of the condition that has caused their disability. This is evident in the way that disabled people are sometimes referred to by their disease or condition: for example, 'he's a Down's syndrome' or 'she's an epileptic'.

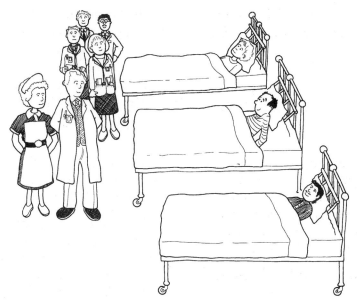

'Now we have a stroke in Bed 1, an MS in Bed 2 and a Parkinson's in Bed 3 – yes?'

Figure 2.3   An extreme example of the medical model in practice

Its usefulness is apparent where an individual has recently sustained a permanent impairment (e.g. Roger's case study on page 66). In the early stages of Roger's injury, medical intervention and rehabilitation were vital to establish new skills in body management. However, doctors are given a significant administrative role in the care and management of disability, and a variety of specialist professions have developed with a publicly visible role as gatekeepers to medical, social and welfare services. When we turn to examine the service provision for disabled people, the limitations of the medical model become apparent. By focusing on the *disability* of the individual rather than the *ability*, a climate of dependency is fostered where many disabled people are cared for in institutions. As long as there is no medical cure or solution to the problem, disabled people are inherently 'socially dead' and permanently dependent upon others for their care in the community or in an institution.

THE SOCIAL BARRIERS MODEL

The main criticism of official definitions of disability is that they fail to take account of the views of disabled people and see them as passive subjects. Most experts in this field now recognise the need for disabled people to become involved in research and particularly in the design process. Finkelstein asserted that if the physical and social world were adapted for wheelchair users, their disabilities would disappear and *able-bodied* people would become disabled.

The social barriers model emphasises the need to change society – removing real barriers to equality of opportunity. The extent of medical interventions should be guided by an analysis of the social and

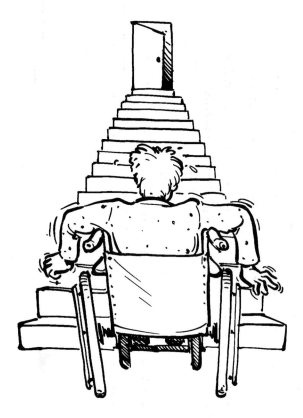

Figure 2.4 The real barrier

personal barriers to be overcome, rather than by any functional limitations of the individual. The following changes are suggested:

- The Department of the Environment should be the main agency for organising disability-related services in the community. This would enhance the role of disciplines such as engineering and architecture in the lives of disabled people.
- Such services should no longer be service-led but provided as a resource with clear access rights for disabled people.
- Centres for Integrated Living (CILs), which are run by disabled people, should provide guidance for all services used by disabled people, including medical, educational, housing and transport services.

- Those responsible for providing services for disabled people (the service providers) should place *less* emphasis on functional assessment of disability and *more* emphasis on designing appropriate intervention (service) models. This shift of emphasis would lead to better identification and subsequent removal of barriers.
- Civil rights legislation should be enacted to provide a framework for guiding the development of community-based support systems for disabled people living in their own homes and to ensure equal opportunities in employment and equal access to education and medical services, housing, leisure, the environment and information.

INTEGRATED LIVING SUPPORT MODEL

This approach to service provision is closely linked to the social barriers model. It searches for new ways to engage disabled people more actively in their own concerns, and to encourage new forms of cooperative or self-help. The people who would decide on the type of services or care systems would not be doctors or social welfare personnel; rather, systems would be set up which actively involve disabled people in dismantling the physical and social barriers created by society. The Independent Living Movement has pioneered this approach to service provision (see page 33). There are now approximately 200 CILs in the USA and 7 in Great Britain. The ways in which CILs promote independence are:

- they are organisations *of*, not *for* disabled people
- disability is made more visible

WHO or welfare model	Medical model	Social barriers model	Integrated living support model
Disease	Disability medically defined	Disability created by attitudes in society	Disability created by attitudes in society
Impairment (parts or systems of the body that do not work)	View of disability as personal tragedy	Disability created by social barriers	Disability created by social barriers
Disability (things people cannot do)	Physical explanation to account for disability	Discrimination more a problem than physical or mental impairment	Dependency assumed on part of disabled people
Handicap (social and economic disadvantage)	No medical cure, therefore disability seen as 'social death'	Exclusion and segregation of disabled people is main problem	Lack of autonomy and independence of disabled people seen as main problem
Social dimension recognised	Dependency of disabled people results	Independence of disabled people encouraged	Active involvement of disabled people results in greater autonomy
Service provision is decided by health and social care personnel	Service provision is decided by health personnel	Service provision is decided by disabled people	Service provision is decided by disabled people in organised systems

Table 2.1   A summary of models of disability

- disabled people have more control in service provision
- more emphasis is placed on *personal growth* and away from any dependent role.

SOCIAL DEVIANCY MODEL OF DISABILITY

This model depends on the process of labelling. An adult who is over 6 feet 8 inches or under 4 feet 6 inches tall may be described as *physically deviant* from the normative height measurement; however, he is not described as *socially deviant* unless his behaviour is equally 'abnormal'. An outstanding musician or scientific genius is regarded as deviant, but is highly regarded. A person with multiple disabilities is also deviant but not regarded as a valuable member of society. There are two concepts of deviance, primary and secondary.

Primary deviance

This concept relates to the labelling of a state of behaviour as deviant; it separates and labels behaviour into what is socially acceptable or unacceptable.

For example, glossolalia – or 'speaking in unknown tongues' – is a common feature of religious practices all over the world. It usually takes place within a church and at a specified time. To those who believe in glossolalia, it is thought to arise from a supernatural power entering into the individual and controlling the organs of speech. In context, this behaviour is socially acceptable and therefore not socially deviant. However, if a student in your class were to stand up, close her eyes and start to utter incomprehensible words, her behaviour would be unacceptable and classed as socially deviant.

Secondary deviance

This concept relates to the *effect* that the labelling has on the individual's behaviour. Being labelled or stereotyped tends to encourage conformity with the label, thereby becoming a 'self-fulfilling prophecy' (see page 8).

For example, a patient in hospital who is always referred to by staff as 'difficult and demanding' is more likely to evoke certain reactions from the staff who care for him which perpetuate the 'difficult' behaviour. Similarly, if a teacher is told that certain children are very intelligent, even if they are of medium ability, those 'labelled' children will achieve better results than children of supposed lesser ability.

Implications for service provision

Once labelled, an individual may change his or her behaviour to conform to the public stereotype that fits the label; for example, a man fully recovered from a heart attack may respond to the public image of a 'coronary cripple' by refusing to return to work or leave the house. The response of health and social care services has been to segregate the 'social deviants' in large institutions where they are encouraged to fulfil the role assigned to them. This inevitably leads to *institutionalisation*, where it becomes increasingly difficult for the individuals to function normally outside the home or hospital. The implications for disabled people are greater for those with learning difficulties and mental illness than for those with physical disabilities. The loss of autonomy and independence by people with learning difficulties is often seen to be a necessary consequence of society's need to be protected from those who cannot function adequately in the wider community. (Care

in the community is discussed in Chapter 6.)

Models of residential care

The ways in which health and social care staff in institutions view elderly and disabled people constitutes their *value system*. The type of value system present in any institution will directly determine the type of care provided. Staff who are committed to preserving life at all costs will adopt the warehousing model of care, whereas staff who define the residents as normal will adopt the horticultural model.

THE WAREHOUSING MODEL

The main purpose in this form of residential care is to prolong physical life. Staff are employed to provide physical care, such as feeding, washing and toileting clients, in a routine manner. The term likens client care to the storage of furniture in a warehouse; clients are encouraged to be *dependent* and *depersonalised*. Any assertion of independence by clients is discouraged because it would disrupt the primary routine task of physical care. Some elderly person's homes still exhibit this kind of care – chairs arranged in rows with understimulated occupants.

THE HORTICULTURAL MODEL

The main purpose in this form of care is the opposite to warehousing: the client is positively encouraged to become *independent*. The main task is to develop the individual's potential. This is normally attempted through organising social activities and providing a 'home-like' environ-

ment. Clients who are mentally confused or who have learning difficulties are encouraged to interact with others and to become more independent.

THE NORMALISATION MODEL

This model was proposed by Wolfensberger in 1972. As the name implies, normalisation emphasises the need to integrate people into the wider society – to provide as normal a life as possible, often in small 'sheltered' group homes where support is provided by a professional care worker. The practice of putting people with disabilities and elderly people in institutions led to them being undervalued and stereotyped. It also perpetuated the notion that people with disabilities have less right to be valued for themselves than others.

THE SOCIAL ROLE VALORISATION MODEL

Wolfensberger later refined and renamed the normalisation model as social role valorisation. Key features of this model are:

- People with learning difficulties should not be hidden away, but be part of the wider community.
- Individuals should be encouraged to develop their skills and so increase their confidence to function effectively in 'normal' situations.

- People with learning difficulties should be encouraged to understand their situation and to make their own decisions and choices.
- Individuals should participate fully in society and have a wide network of relationships.
- Society must value and respect people

with learning difficulties rather than viewing them as second-class citizens.

This model has been influential in shaping the current policy of care in the community, but most experts in the field would agree that attitudes and stereotyping take a long time to change.

Model of Care	Main Features	Effects on clients or patients
Warehousing model	Physical care seen as paramount. Care is given according to a set routine, which may ignore the social and emotional needs of the recipient	Clients or patients become dependent and depersonalised
Horticultural model	Every effort is made to provide an environment as close to a 'real home' as possible. Developing the client's full potential is paramount	Clients or patients enjoy a range of social activities and are encouraged to become more independent
Normalisation model	Life for the 'resident' should be as near normal as possible; ideally, people are integrated into society by providing small units or homes with professional support	Clients or patients experience higher self-esteem and feel themselves to be part of the wider environment
Social role valorisation model	Similar to normalisation model, but with more emphasis on the development of skills for living and the need for a radical change in attitudes to those with learning disabilities	Clients or patients enjoy maximum possible independence and increased confidence in their own abilities

Table 2.2   A summary of models of residential care

Models of parent–professional relationships

For many years parents of children with special needs were left largely unsupported and received little help from professionals. The focus was almost exclusively on the child and the dominant model was the expert model, described below.

THE EXPERT MODEL

This model is similar to the medical model (see page 34) in that the relationship between professional and parent is defined by the position of the professional as expert. The parents of a disabled child were expected to defer to professional judgement, as the expert always knows best. Professional reports could be written and case conferences could be arranged without parental involvement and access. There has been a move away from the expert model since the 1970s, and the Children Act 1989 further emphasised the rights and expertise of parents.

THE TRANSPLANT MODEL

In this model, parents are perceived by professionals as an untapped resource for helping in the therapy of the disabled child and the home is seen as a potentially important learning setting. Professionals share or transplant their skills and expertise to parents, to help them to become more competent, confident and skilled. Parents are assisted to become actively involved and to participate in the role of co-teachers. The Portage programme is an example of this model in practice (see page 198).

THE CONSUMER MODEL

This model was developed by Cunningham and Davis (1985); it outlines the importance of a shift in power from the professional to the parent. The parent would be given new resource power, with some control over access to resources. This shift in power means that the professional's influence would become more one of exchange and negotiation. The professional's function would be to guide the parent in reaching effective and appropriate decisions.

THE EMPOWERMENT MODEL

In this model, the right of the parent as a consumer is combined with the recognition on the professional side that the family is a system and a social network. Each family is made up of interlocking social relationships, within the family itself and also with wider social groups, e.g. extended family and cultural groups. Because some parents may find it difficult to take up a position as a partner, a form of client empowerment is advocated. The professional would need to promote the parent's sense of control over decisions affecting their child and to be sensitive to parents' rights to get involved in professional services to an extent that they choose.

THE NEGOTIATING MODEL

This model recognises that the parent and the professional have separate and potentially highly valuable contributions to

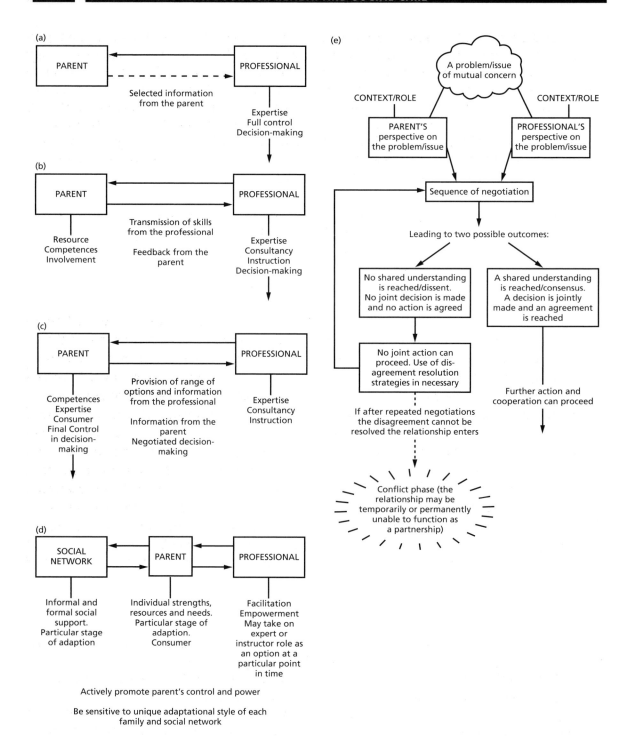

Figure 2.5 Methods of parent–professional relationships (a) the expert model (b) the transplant model (c) the consumer model (d) the empowerment model (e) the negotiating model

Source: Naomi Dale (1996) *Working with Families of Children with Special Needs*, Routledge

offer to children with special needs and other family members, so each may requires the contribution of the other. The position or role taken by the professional in relation to the parent is one that is negotiated with the parent. Both professional and parent are seen as bringing often very different perspectives to the decision-making process. Because of differences between role positions and perspectives, the working partnership may not be easily achieved. Conflict may arise from these differences, but that does not mean that the partnership is doomed; rather, it focuses on the necessity for being willing to adapt and to try to find new ways of reaching a negotiating relationship.

CASE STUDY

A new relationship

A parent sits at home awaiting a new health visitor. She contemplates the arrival with trepidation. 'What will she be like? Will we get on? How will she react to my daughter? Will she be of any help?' She looks across at her young daughter playing on the floor, and recalls some of the many demands and difficulties of cystic fibrosis over the last few years. Then she thinks of the future and is overwhelmed with a sudden surge of anxiety. A long road of uncertainties and worries lies ahead. The door bell rings.

A health visitor drives up to the house of a family she is visiting for the first time. She knows from the case notes that the family has a three-year-old girl with cystic fibrosis. She feels a certain apprehension: 'Will I appear ignorant? I've heard this mother gets anxious and upset, will she be very needy? Do I have enough time to help her?' Her thoughts stray to the many other competing demands of her large caseload, and she gets out of the car feeling stressed and inadequate. She walks to the front door and rings the bell.

activity

Exploring relationships

1 Think about the relationships you have with:
   (a) your tutor or lecturer
   (b) your girl/boyfriend or close intimate friend
   (c) your parents.
2 Write down five statements of how you feel in relationship to each of the people mentioned above.
3 Compare your statements in relation to each person and write down the positive aspects in each relationship that would be important in a relationship between you as a professional and a parent with a child with special needs.

RESOURCES

Mustn't Grumble: Writings by Disabled Women,
edited by Lois Keith, published by
Women's Press (1994). A collection of
poems and prose pieces on illness and
disability.

CHAPTER 3

SPECIAL NEEDS – PHYSICAL DISABILITIES

This chapter is not intended to catalogue the various disorders which often result in disability. It focuses on disorders and conditions which are likely to be encountered in the field of health and social care. Many disabling conditions are caused by complicated genetic or physiological factors and only a brief description of possible causes will be provided. Throughout this chapter and the following chapter, the emphasis will be on the effects on the individual of the more commonly encountered disabilities and on the ways in which carers can help to manage the problems caused by such disabilities.

There are three main ways in which a person can become disabled:

- **hereditary and congenital** – when a faulty gene leads to a disabling condition
- **developmental** – when the foetus is growing in the womb
- **through illness or accident** – affecting individuals who are born with no disability.

Hereditary conditions

Growth and development of the embryo and fetus are controlled by *genes*. The influence of our genes is almost too great to comprehend. They determine everything from eye colour to body shape and even affect intelligence and personality. In 1953, two Cambridge scientists, James Watson and Francis Crick, identified a chemical called deoxyribonucleic acid (DNA). DNA molecules are made up of hundreds of thousands of smaller units joined together like a necklace. Each 'bead' is a sequence of three units and holds the code for one of 20 *amino-acids*, which are the basic building blocks of proteins. When a unit is 'switched on', it is

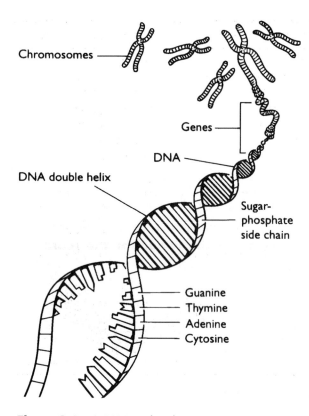

Figure 3.1 A DNA molecule

decoded so that an amino acid can be made. These join together to form bigger and bigger proteins, ready to move out of the cell and perform their function in the body.

Each of us inherits two copies of all our genes – one from each parent. For ordinary tasks, like producing insulin, the two copies should be the same. Only the genes which hold the code for more personal aspects of our make-up will routinely be markedly different.

DOMINANT GENE DEFECTS

A dominant gene from one parent will take precedence over whatever equivalent gene is inherited from the other parent. If it is a faulty gene, the result is whatever disorder it codes for. Examples of dominant gene defects are:

- Huntington's disease
- tuberous sclerosis
- achondroplasia
- Marfan's syndrome
- neurofibromatosis.

Huntington's disease

Formerly known as Huntington's chorea, this is a rare brain disorder which affects about 3,000 people in the UK. Individuals who inherit the gene go on to develop **dementia** in later life. Researchers have now discovered that the gene lies on chromosome 4, so they can now test for the defect. Children of a parent who carries the defective gene have a one in two chance of developing the disorder, so someone who finds that they have the defective gene can now decide whether to risk passing it on to their own children.

Tuberous sclerosis

This is a rare disorder affecting the skin and the nervous system; the condition takes its name from the sclerotic (hardened) tuber-shaped areas which calcify and grow slowly in the brain. About 80 per cent of children with tuberous sclerosis develop epilepsy.

Achondroplasia

This disorder was once called dwarfism; it is a rare hereditary disorder of cartilage formation in the foetus.

Marfan's syndrome

This is a rare disorder affecting the connective tissue (material which surrounds body structures and holds them together);

Dominant gene defects		Recessive gene defects		X-linked gene defects	
tuberous sclerosis achondroplasia Huntington's chorea neurofibromatosis Marfan's syndrome		cystic fibrosis Friedreich's ataxia phenylketonuria sickle-cell anaemia Tay-Sachs disease thalassaemia		haemophilia Christmas disease 'fragile X' syndrome muscular dystrophy – Duchenne type colour blindness most types	
Unaffected parent	Affected parent	Unaffected parent (carrier)	Unaffected parent (carrier)	Carrier mother	Unaffected father
○ ○	○ △	○ △	○ △	⊗ ●	Ⓨ ⊗
Unaffected child	Affected child	Unaffected child / Unaffected child (carrier)	Unaffected child (carrier) / Affected child	Unaffected boy / Affected boy	Unaffected girl / Unaffected girl (carrier)
○ ○	○ △	○ ○ ／ ○ △	○ △ ／ △ △	⊗ Ⓨ ／ ● Ⓨ	⊗ ⊗ ／ ● ⊗
1 in 2 chance	1 in 2 chance	1 in 4 chance / 1 in 4 chance	1 in 4 chance / 1 in 4 chance	1 in 4 chance / 1 in 4 chance	1 in 4 chance / 1 in 4 chance

Key: △ = defective gene ○ = normal gene   ● = defective x chromosome   ⊗ = normal x chromosome Ⓨ = y chromosome

Table 3.1   A summary of genetic defects and their pattern of inheritance

it results in abnormalities of the skeleton, heart and eyes.

Neurofibromatosis

This is a rare disorder characterised by numerous neurofibromas (soft, fibrous swellings which grow from nerves) and by pale, coffee-coloured patches on the skin.

RECESSIVE GENE DEFECTS

A recessive gene will only have an effect if a copy is inherited from both parents. Many inherited disorders come under this category. A child who inherits only one copy of the gene will not have the disorder, but may pass it on to his or her own children – in other words, the child will be a **carrier** of the disorder. If both parents carry a single recessive gene defect, there is a one in four chance that each of their children will be affected. Examples of defects transmitted in this way are:

- cystic fibrosis (CF)
- sickle cell anaemia
- phenylketonuria
- thalassaemia
- Tay-Sachs disease
- Friedreich's ataxia.

Cystic fibrosis

This is an inherited disease which is present from birth. Among Western Europeans and white Americans, the incidence of CF is one per 2,000 live births, and one person in 25 is a carrier of the faulty recessive gene. Features of the disease are:

- an inability to absorb fats and other nutrients from food
- chronic lung infections – bronchitis and pneumonia
- pancreatitis – inflammation of the pancreas
- gallstones – formation of stones in the gall bladder
- liver problems
- diabetes – a disorder caused by insufficient production of the hormone insulin by the pancreas
- infertility in most males and some females
- heatstroke and collapse may occur in hot climates due to excessive loss of salt in the sweat.

Recent research has succeeded in locating the gene that causes CF. It is now possible to detect the carrier state and also to test for CF before birth. Once CF is suspected in the young baby, simple laboratory tests, including an analysis of sweat content, will confirm or refute the diagnosis. Recently there has been a call to **screen** all newborn babies for CF – as is already done for the rare condition, phenylketonuria – as early detection and treatment greatly improves the chances of recovery.

Treatment and care include:

- intensive physiotherapy
- diet rich in calories and proteins, usually with vitamin supplements
- pancreatin (a replacement pancreatic enzyme preparation) given with meals to enable food to be properly digested.

The recurrence of severe respiratory infections often means that CF sufferers have permanent lung damage. Lung transplants are sometimes offered and can prolong life expectancy.

CASE STUDY

A person with cystic fibrosis

My name is Lisa and I have cystic fibrosis. I was diagnosed with CF when I was two months old. The doctors did a sweat test and were able to confirm that I had CF because children with CF produce more salt than other children. Mostly, what having CF means to me is that I have chest problems. Mucus grows in my lungs; healthy lungs have tiny hairs to clean out the mucus but mine don't. So I have to have physiotherapy to get it all cleared out. I find this a real pain. For 20 minutes before school and last thing at night, I have to exercise my lungs by blowing into a mask really hard – the dial has to reach a certain level. Even when I am on holiday or at a friend's house overnight, I have to do these exercises. The equipment takes up quite a lot of room so I always look as though I've got more stuff than anyone else when I go away. I used to have to have postural drainage and physiotherapy when I was younger. I was lucky that both Mum and Dad got really expert at doing the squeezing and tapping exercises.

Another problem is that my digestive

system doesn't digest food properly. This means that I have to take quite big tablets called creon, which supply the acid needed to help break down my food. I have to take 10 tablets every time I eat a proper meal and 6 or 8 tablets when I have a snack.

I have to take quite a lot of medication generally – including nebulisers to help me breathe more easily. The nebuliser works by a compressor. This delivers a mist containing tiny droplets of the drugs which can get right down into my lungs where they are needed. [Note, some asthmatic patients also take their drugs via a nebuliser.] If in spite of all my exercises and medication, I get a chest infection, then I have to go into hospital for intravenous antibiotics.

One other side-effect of CF is that it can cause liver disease, which is something I had. Last year I had a liver transplant and I feel so much better now. I've got more energy and I can now wear normal jeans. Before the transplant, the liver disease made my stomach stick out and it was hard to find clothes to wear.

One other effect of having CF is that I don't have as much energy as other people my age. At school, there are lots of stairs, which makes my legs ache and can make me late for lessons. My friends all accept me as I am, but when I meet new people, they often ask lots of questions. For me, having CF is part of my life. It all sounds pretty terrible when you put it on paper, but it doesn't really stop me doing things other children do. It seems completely normal – I don't know what life is without it.

activity

This 'snapshot' case study of a person with cystic fibrosis gives some insight into the reality of life with CF for Lisa, but it tells us little about the impact of CF on the family or about the network of caregivers which makes life easier for the family.

1 Find out what help is available to Lisa's family from:
   (a) the NHS
   (b) social services
   (c) the private care sector
   (d) voluntary organisations.
2 Find out what educational provision Lisa might need if she has to spend more time in hospital.
3 What help do you think the Cystic Fibrosis Research Trust can offer Lisa and her family?
4 In Britain, 1 in 20 of the population are carriers; the chance of two carriers becoming partners in 1 in 400. What is the chance of a child of two carriers having a child with cystic fibrosis (see Table 3.1)? Should Tom, Lisa's brother, be worried that he may be a carrier and can he be genetically tested?

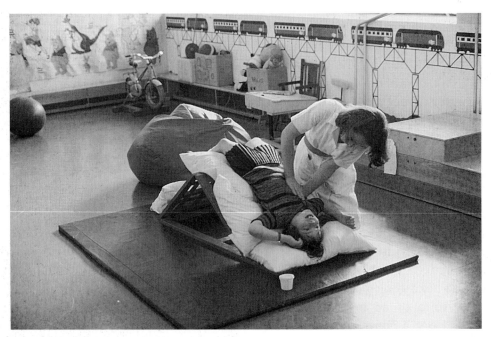

Figure 3.2 Postural drainage and physiotherapy for cystic fibrosis

Guidelines for care

- Children with CF can join in with whatever the other children are doing, but they have to remember their physiotherapy, enzymes and exercise programmes.
- The lungs of a child with CF must be kept clear to prevent infection. Try to learn how to perform the necessary postural drainage and physiotherapy techniques involved (see Figure 3.2).
- Children with CF can eat a normal diet but need to take enzyme and vitamin supplements; they may also need salt tablets if they are undertaking strenuous exercise in hot weather.
- They may tire easily but should be encouraged to take lots of exercise to keep healthy. Good exercises are running, swimming, cycling and skipping.

Note: Always obtain permission from the child's parents or guardians before performing any of the techniques outlined above.

Sickle cell anaemia

Sickle cell anaemia is an inherited blood disorder caused by abnormal **haemoglobin**. The red blood cells (normally round) become sickle- or crescent-shaped. The cells clump together and lodge in the smaller blood vessels, preventing normal blood flow and resulting in anaemia (lack of haemoglobin).

In Britain sickle cell anaemia is most common in people of African or Caribbean descent, but may also occur in people from India, Pakistan, the Middle East and the Eastern Mediterranean.

Features of sickle cell anaemia

Children with sickle cell anaemia can almost always attend a mainstream school but are subject to *crises* which may include:

- **pain** – often severe, occurring in the arms, legs, back and stomach, due to the blockage to normal blood flow
- **infections** – children are most susceptible to coughs, colds, sore throats, fever and other infectious diseases
- **anaemia** – most children are anaemic; only if it is severe will they feel lethargic and ill
- **jaundice** – may show as yellow staining of the whites of the eyes.

Guidelines for care

Blood transfusions may be necessary. Infections should be treated promptly and immunisation against all the normal childhood diseases is recommended.

- Know how to recognise a crisis. If the child suddenly becomes unwell or complains of severe abdominal or chest pain, headache, neck stiffness or drowsiness, contact the child's parents without delay – the child needs urgent hospital treatment.
- Make sure the child is always warm and dry. Never let a child with sickle cell anaemia get chilled after PE or swimming.
- Make sure the child does not become dehydrated – allow him or her to drink more often and much more than normal.
- Make sure that the child is fully immunised against infectious illnesses and that any prescribed medicines (e.g. vitamins and antibiotics) are given.
- Give support – the child may find it difficult to come to terms with the condition; make allowances when necessary.

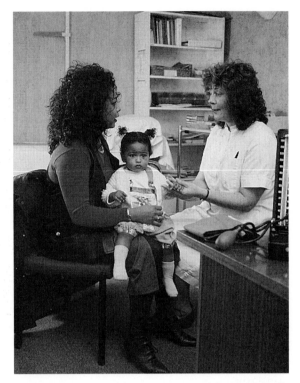

Figure 3.3   A child being assessed for sickle cell anaemia

- Help with schoolwork – if badly anaemic, the child may find it difficult to concentrate and regular visits to the GP or hospital may entail many days off school.

Phenylketonuria

Phenylketonuria is a very rare metabolic disorder, which prevents the normal use of protein food. If untreated, it usually damages the nervous system and leads to mental retardation. It affects around 1 in 10,000 babies in the UK. All babies born in the UK are routinely tested for phenylketonuria by means of a simple blood test

– the Guthrie Test. A small blood sample is taken from the baby's heel when about 7–11 days old and is sent for analysis to a central laboratory. Early diagnosis is vital and treatment involves a special formula protein diet which has to be followed throughout the person's life.

Thalassaemia

Thalassaemia is a group of inherited blood disorders in which there is a fault in the production of haemoglobin. Many of the red cells produced are fragile and are rapidly broken up, leading to anaemia. Thalassaemia is prevalent in the Mediterranean region, the Middle East and South East Asia, and in families originating from these areas. The difficulties experienced by people with this disorder are similar to those of sickle cell anaemia.

Tay-Sachs disease

Tay-Sachs disease is a serious inherited metabolic disorder. It is caused by a deficiency of hexosaminidase A, an enzyme which is essential for regulating chemical reactions within the body. Deficiency of this enzyme results in a build-up of a harmful substance in the brain. Tay-Sachs disease is most common among Ashkenazi Jews, in which ethnic group the incidence is 1 in 2,500 births, over 100 times higher than in any other group. There is no effective treatment for the disease and death usually occurs in early childhood.

Friedreich's ataxia

This is a very rare inherited disease of the central nervous system in which there is a progressive deterioration of coordination and muscle control (ataxia). Friedreich's ataxia usually appears before adolescence and is characterised by clumsy hand movements, unsteadiness when walking and slurred speech. The incidence is about 1 in 50,000 in the UK. Intelligence is unaffected, but people with Friedreich's ataxia are more likely to have heart disease or diabetes than the general population.

X-LINKED RECESSIVE GENE DEFECTS

In these conditions, the defective gene is on the X chromosome and usually leads to outward abnormality in males only. Women can be carriers of the defect and half their sons may be affected. Examples are:

- haemophilia
- Christmas disease
- 'fragile X' syndrome (see page 104)
- muscular dystrophy (Duchenne type)

Haemophilia

Haemophilia is a term used to describe a group of inherited blood disorders in which there is a life-long defect in one of the clotting factors which cause blood to coagulate and therefore stop bleeding. The clotting factors are numbered I to XIII; the commonest defect occurs in factor VIII. **Christmas disease** affects factor IX. Bleeding will occur for much longer than normal after injury or operations. The severity of the disorder differs markedly among affected individuals. Most bleeding episodes involve bleeding into joints and muscles, which causes a great deal of pain.

The use of factor VIII has considerably improved the quality of life for many people with haemophilia, but relies on the use of blood donations. A percentage of people have unfortunately received blood contaminated by **viral hepatitis** and the **HIV virus**, and many have died of **AIDS**. All blood donations are now screened to prevent transmission of HIV by transfusion, and factor VIII is heat-treated to kill any virus that slips through the detection system.

Muscular dystrophy

There are more than 20 types of muscular dystrophy. The best known type is *Duchenne muscular dystrophy*. It is a muscle wasting disorder linked to a gene on the X chromosome. Women are often carriers of the defective gene, but the disease affects only boys. The incidence of Duchenne muscular dystrophy is about 1 in 3,500 boys. In the UK about two boys per week are born with the disorder.

Duchenne muscular dystrophy results from a single important protein in muscle fibres called *dystrophin*. Every one of the billions of cells forming the muscle fibres is affected, making their repair a huge logistical challenge.

The slow, progressive breakdown of the muscle fibres over several years leads to the destruction of the muscle tissues. The child is slow in learning to sit up and to walk. Although the muscles are weak, they often appear bulky because the wasted muscle is replaced by fat and fibrous tissue. By the age of about 10 or 11 years, the boy is often unable to walk and will need the assistance of a wheelchair.

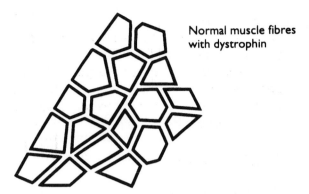

Normal muscle fibres with dystrophin

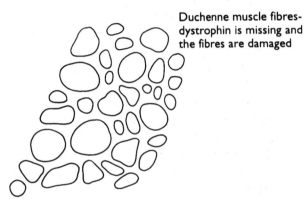

Duchenne muscle fibres- dystrophin is missing and the fibres are damaged

Figure 3.4   Normal muscle fibres compared with Duchenne muscle fibres

Exercise and physiotherapy are vital to the maintenance of muscle strength. Sometimes the muscles of the back are affected, resulting in curvature of the spine (scoliosis). Eventually, the respiratory muscles become weak and this leads to death from a chest infection or heart failure.

CASE STUDY

Access to education

Liam was diagnosed with Duchenne muscular dystrophy when he was just two. He is now seven years old and uses a wheelchair. The Local Education Authority (LEA) offered Liam a place at his local mainstream primary school, dependent on the provision of a full-time classroom assistant to help ensure the safety of Liam, who weighs just three stone and is partially sighted. To obtain this provision, the LEA required that Liam be **statemented**. This process took several months. Meanwhile Liam's classmates moved up to a classroom on the first floor for many of their regular activities and Liam, who was unable to join them, has been – according to his hospital report – 'profoundly affected emotionally by being separated from his peer group'. The head teacher has always been very supportive. Liam is an intelligent boy who needs a full education and could obviously receive one if a lift were installed. His parents are fighting the LEA's refusal to fit a lift at the school. They feel that Liam is being marginalised or punished for having a disability.

activity

1 Read the case study above. What can Liam's parents do to ensure that he receives the help he needs?

2 The Muscular Dystrophy Group has led a campaign called 'Batteries Not Included' which lobbied parliament to provide indoor/outdoor electric wheelchairs. Find out about other organisations which fight for the rights of disabled people. Write a report of your findings.

3 Research the range of services available in your own local authority for disabled children and their families.

Figure 3.5 The campaign logo from the Muscular Dystrophy Group

CHROMOSOMAL DEFECTS

These vary considerably in the severity of their effect on the individual. About 1 in every 200 babies born alive has a chromosomal abnormality, i.e. the structure or number of chromosomes differs from normal. Among foetuses that have been spontaneously aborted (miscarried), about one in two has such an abnormality. This suggests that most chromosomal abnormalities are incompatible with life, and that those seen in babies born alive are generally the less serious ones. Examples of defects transmitted this way are:

- Down's syndrome – described in Chapter 4
- Klinefelter's syndrome – boys are very tall with **hypogonadism** (underactivity of the testes)
- Turner's syndrome – girls have a webbed neck, are short in stature and may not develop sexually; they may also have cardiac malfunctions
- cri du chat syndrome – a very rare condition in which a portion of one particular chromosome is missing in each of the affected individual's cells.

GENE THERAPY

It is estimated that humans have between 50,000 and 100,000 different genes; some of these are linked to particular diseases or conditions. Scientists have now identified nearly 4,000 conditions that are linked to single defects in a person's genetic code. Researchers around the world are currently engaged in 'The Human Genome Project' which aims to identify and define the function of every gene to be found in the human body. Through this, they hope to locate errant genes, thereby gaining a better understanding of every disease that

is genetically transmittable and, if possible, find a cure for it. Genetic engineering, whereby the defective gene sequence is cut and remodelled, is one route scientists might take.

In February 1997, scientists succeeded for the first time in making a clone – an exact copy – of an adult animal. Dolly, a Finn Dorset lamb, is the identical twin of her genetic mother. She was created by scientists taking a single cell from her mother's udders and planting it into another sheep's egg from which the genetic material had been removed. The successful cloning has raised new concerns about the ethics of genetic engineering. Dr Patrick Dixon, author of *The Genetic Revolution*, suggests that almost any technique that can be performed on an animal can be reproduced on a human. He states that possible uses of cloning in humans might include:

- people with serious illnesses who want to create the perfect match for transplant surgery
- parents who fear losing a child to cot death
- film producers who want to re-create dead stars.

THE EUGENICS MOVEMENT

Eugenics is the doctrine and study of improving the population by controlled breeding for desirable inherited characteristics. Advocates of eugenics seek either to promote the procreation of supposedly superior human beings or to prevent the procreation of supposedly inferior human beings. It was a philosophy which flourished under Hitler and Nazism in Germany, when the German people were encouraged to think of theirs as the superior race and to eliminate non-Aryans, principally the Jewish people. In spite of the revulsion most people feel towards the eugenics movement as it applied during the 1940s in Europe, eugenic principles still underlie practices all over the world, for example:

- selective sterilisation of young adults with severe learning difficulties
- denial of the right of people with disabilities to have children

- the offer of amniocentesis and the option of termination of pregnancy (abortion) if the results show a chromosomal abnormality
- the recent prohibition by the Chinese government of all those with 'unhealthy genes' from having babies.

activity

Predicting health and preventing disease

1 As testing of the unborn child for genetic influences progresses, would you put limits on the process?
2 Some women, having been told after genetic testing that they are likely to develop breast cancer, have opted for a radical mastectomy (surgery to remove the breast) in order to increase their chances of survival. What problems can you foresee if the inspection of an individual's DNA for imperfections becomes a routine practice? Does the wish to improve our individual genetic profile somehow diminish the meaning of the lives of people who are born with a genetic disorder?

GENETIC COUNSELLING

Genetic counselling is the process of support and the giving of advice to anyone who has either experienced the birth of a baby with a congenital abnormality, e.g. spina bifida or congenital heart disease, or who runs the risk that any child born to them may suffer from a genetically transmitted disorder, e.g. where there is a history of hereditary disease such as Duchenne muscular dystrophy.

Genetic counsellors may use any of the following sources of information:

- If the parents already have an affected child, it is easier for them to predict the likelihood of the next child or children being similarly affected.
- Pedigree analysis involves the examination of a family tree showing affected members of the family.
- The frequency of the gene in the population as a whole indicates the likely *genotype* of the spouse. (A person's genotype refers to the genes they possess; the term *phenotype* describes the physical characteristics determined by the genes.)
- If the prospective parents are related to each other, they are more likely to have inherited the same gene.
- For some genetic diseases, a sample of blood or cheek cells can be tested with a

DNA probe to test for the presence of the harmful **allele**. In this way, carriers of the disease can be identified.

The aim of genetic counselling is not to make decisions for people but to enable them to have the necessary understanding of the situation so that they can reach a decision for themselves. It is carried out by someone with a medical or nursing background who has had further training in both genetics and counselling, or by someone who has been specially trained as a genetics counsellor. Once any risks have been identified, the genetic counsellor will discuss the options available to the couple. These options will be influenced by the moral and religious beliefs of the couple and their cultural background. They may include:

- not having children
- using **in vitro fertilisation (IVF)** so that the cells of the embryo can be screened for genetic abnormalities before implantation; with sex-linked diseases, a female embryo may be selected for implantation
- using egg, sperm or embryo donation
- terminating the pregnancy if foetal screening shows abnormalities.

Developmental disorders

The first three months (the first trimester of a pregnancy) are when the foetus is particularly vulnerable. The lifestyle of the pregnant woman affects the health of the baby in her womb. Important factors are:

- a healthy diet
- not smoking
- avoiding alcohol and the use of other drugs
- taking regular, appropriate exercise.

RUBELLA

Rubella ('German measles') is particularly harmful to the developing foetus as it can cause deafness, blindness and severe learning disability. All girls in the UK are now immunised against rubella before they reach childbearing age – usually at age 12 or 13 – and this measure has dramatically reduced the incidence of rubella-damaged babies.

TOXOPLASMOSIS

Toxoplasmosis is an infection caused by the protozoan *Toxoplasma gondi*. There are several ways in which the pregnant woman may contract this infection:

- by eating raw or undercooked meat (usually pork) from infected animals
- by handling dirty cat litter and garden soil contaminated with cat faeces and urine
- by eating contaminated fruit and vegetables
- by eating unpasteurised dairy products.

In about one-third of cases, toxoplasmosis is transmitted to the foetus and may cause blindness, hydrocephalus or severe learning disability. Infection in late pregnancy usually has no ill effects. The overall rate of infection in pregnant women is 2 per 1,000, i.e. approximately 1,400 women every year. Almost half of these women will pass the infection on to their children, resulting in over 500 babies in the UK being born infected by toxoplasmosis.

THALIDOMIDE

Thalidomide was a drug widely prescribed during the 1960s to relieve morning sickness in pregnant women. Unfortunately, it was found to cause limb deformities in many of the babies born to women who had used the drug, and was withdrawn in 1961. *Phocomelia* was the most common of these deformities; phocomelia is a limb defect in which the feet and/or the hands are joined to the trunk by a small irregularly shaped bone.

IRRADIATION

If a woman is X-rayed in early pregnancy, or if she receives radiotherapy for the treatment of cancer, the embryo may suffer abnormalities. Radiation damage may also result from atomic radiation or radioactive fall-out (following a nuclear explosion or leak from a nuclear reactor). There is also an increased risk of the child developing leukaemia in later life after exposure to radiation.

SPINA BIFIDA

Spina bifida refers to a malformation of the spine in which part of one or more **vertebrae** fails to develop completely, leaving a portion of the **spinal cord** exposed. (Bifid literally means split.)

The fault usually occurs within the first month of pregnancy and may appear anywhere on the spine's length, although it is most common at about waist level. It is the most common disability apparent at birth; in the UK the incidence is 1.5 per 1,000.

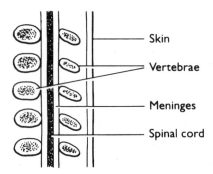

Cervical nerves
use of neck, shoulders and arms

Thoracic nerves
Use of hands and fingers, chest and abdomen, lower back and hip

Lumbar nerves
Use of seat muscles to keep body erect, leg, knee and foot and ejaculation (in men)

Sacrum nerves
Bowel and bladder and control of erection (in men)

Skin

Vertebrae

Meninges

Spinal cord

Figure 3.6   The spinal column, showing the nerves which control the movement of different parts of the body

There are three main forms of spina bifida (see Figure 3.7).

1 **Spina bifida occulta** is the most common and the least serious form. It often goes completely unnoticed unless detected by X-ray, and rarely causes disability. Often the only exterior sign

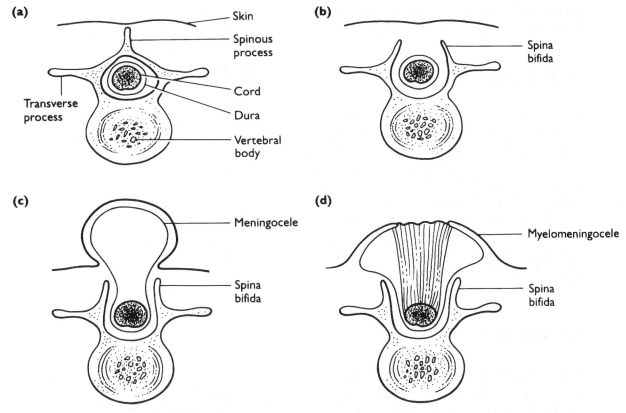

Figure 3.7 Spina bifida (a) Normal canal with spinous processes projecting posteriorly (b) Spina bifida occulat – no involvement of the meninges or spinal cord (c) Meningocele – showing spina bifida and involvement of the meninges (d) Myelomeningocele – showing spina bifida, meningeal involvement and exposed nervous tissue

of spina bifida is a dimple or tuft of hair on the sacral area of the back. The spinal cord and meninges are unaffected.

2 **Meningocele** shows as a sac or cyst on the back, covered by a thin layer of skin. The sac is composed of the meninges which protrude through the split (bifid) vertebrae. As the spinal cord and nervous tissue are unaffected, there are usually no functional problems.

3 **Myelomeningocele** is the most severe form of spina bifida and is more common than meningocele. The sac contains not only meningeal tissue and cerebrospinal fluid, but also nerves and part of the spinal cord itself. The legs may be partly or completely paralysed (paraplegia) and there may also be loss of skin sensation to pain, temperature and touch in all areas below the level of the defect. Blood circulation may be poor and congenital dislocation of the hip is common.

Hydrocephalus (commonly known as 'water on the brain') occurs in more than 80 per cent of babies born with spina bifida. It is caused by an excessive accumulation of cerebrospinal fluid under increased pressure within the skull. To prevent brain damage, the extra fluid must be drained by means of a tube inserted through a hole made in the skull. (Note: hydrocephalus may also develop as a result of major head injury, brain haemorrhage, infection (e.g. meningitis) or a brain tumour.)

Diagnosis and treatment of spina bifida

Myelomeningocele may be diagnosed at an early stage of pregnancy by **ultrasound scanning**. High levels of alpha-fetoprotein in the amniotic fluid or in the pregnant mother's blood may also indicate spina bifida. **CT scanning** and **Magnetic Resonance Imaging (MRI)** show the location and nature of any obstruction in the event of hydrocephalus.

Care needs of people with spina bifida

Most people with severe spina bifida are incontinent of urine and may require artificial control in the form of **catheterisation** (see page 155). Substantial extra attention is required to care for the skin, as areas of decreased sensation have a tendency to break down. The use of air mattresses, sheepskin and other similar materials may help to prevent the breakdown of skin tissue. Most people with spina bifida have average intellectual ability despite hydrocephalus and are usually able to attend a mainstream school, provided they are able to overcome other barriers (architectural and attitudinal). Surgery to close the open **lesion** and/or remove the sac can usually be done soon after birth.

Hydrocephalus can produce squints and poor hand coordination. The need to monitor the drainage of excess fluid from the brain often results in frequent periods of hospitalisation.

Some common problems associated with severe spina bifida are:

- **Infection**: urinary and/or faecal incontinence increases the risk of infection, as does the development of pressure sores.
- **Skin breakdown:** skin is particularly vulnerable because of decreased sensation and the effects of reduced mobility.
- **Obesity or excessive weight gain**: inactivity enforced by long periods spent in a wheelchair often leads to excessive weight gain; dietary control is important.
- **Body-image concerns**: As the child grows, there may be increasing concerns over physical appearance, difficulties with mobility and lack of control over excretory functions.
- **Prolonged dependence**: this is related to the reliance on others for help with physical care and with getting around; being able to exercise choice in when and where one will go each day will pose difficulties.
- **Stress within the family**: this is related to the long-term demands of caring for a person with severe disabilities.

activity

An integrated approach to care

A group of health and social care personnel should be available to the child with spina bifida and his or her family. This will usually comprise:

- a neurologist
- a neurosurgeon
- a urologist
- an orthopaedic surgeon
- a paediatrician

- a nurse
- a dietician
- a physiotherapist
- an occupational therapist
- a social worker
- a health visitor

1 Find out what role each of the above would fulfil in relation to a nine-year-old girl with severe myelomeningocele. How can continuity of care best be achieved?

2 Find out about the work of the Association for Spina Bifida and Hydrocephalus (ASBAH). How can the ASBAH help a family caring for a child with severe myelomeningocele? (See 'Useful addresses' section on page 213.)

CEREBRAL PALSY

This is the general term for disorders of movement and posture resulting from injury to a child's developing brain in the later months of pregnancy, during birth, in the **neonatal** period, or in early childhood. The injury does not damage the child's muscles or the nerves which connect them to the spinal cord – only the brain's ability to control the muscles. (Palsy literally means paralysis.)

Cerebral palsy affects 2–3 people in every 1,000. In Britain, about 1,500 babies are born with or develop the condition each year. It can affect boys and girls, and people from all races and social backgrounds.

Causes

The most common cause of cerebral palsy is cerebral hypoxia (poor oxygen supply to the brain). This may occur during pregnancy or around the time of birth. Other causes include:

- an infection in the mother during the first weeks of a baby's development in the womb (e.g. rubella or a **cytomegalovirus**)
- a difficult or **pre-term** birth, perhaps because the baby fails to breathe properly (resulting in cerebral **hypoxia**)
- toxic injury, or poisoning, from drugs or alcohol used by the mother during pregnancy
- infections of the nervous system, such as meningitis or encephalitis
- cerebral bleeding (haematoma) which particularly affects pre-term babies
- bleeding into cavities inside the brain (intra-ventricular haemorrhage) which may occur in pre-term babies
- head trauma resulting from a birth injury, fall, car accident or other causes
- the baby's brain is formed abnormally, for no apparent reason
- a genetic disorder which can be inherited even if both parents are completely healthy.

Types of cerebral palsy

Cerebral palsy jumbles messages between the brain and the muscles. There are three types of cerebral palsy, depending on which messages are affected:

- spastic cerebral palsy
- athetoid cerebral palsy
- ataxic cerebral palsy.

Many people with cerebral palsy have a combination of two or more types. Around 15–40 per cent of people with cerebral palsy have athetosis combined with spasticity and/or ataxia. In some people, cerebral palsy is barely noticeable; others will be more severely affected. No

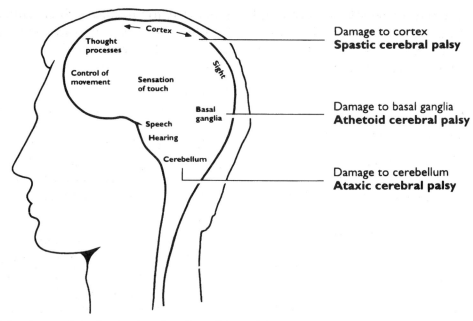

Figure 3.8 Areas of the brain, showing the effects of damage to specific parts

two people will be affected in quite the same way.

Spastic cerebral palsy (spasticity)

With this type the muscles of one or more limbs are permanently contracted and stiff, leading to disordered movement. It is usually caused when nerve cells in the outer layer of the brain (the cortex) do not work properly (see Figure 3.8). About 60 per cent of people with cerebral palsy have this type of disorder. The limbs can be affected as follows:

- **hemiplegia** – both limbs on one side of the body; the arm is usually involved more than the leg
- **diplegia** – all four limbs, but legs are more severely affected than arms
- **paraplegia** – the legs only are involved
- **tetraplegia** or **quadriplegia** – all four limbs severely affected, but not necessarily symmetrically.

Athetoid cerebral palsy (athetosis)

This condition leads to frequent involuntary movements (i.e. movements over which the person has no control). People with this kind of cerebral palsy have muscles which change rapidly from floppy to tense; their speech may be hard to understand because of difficulty in controlling their tongue, breathing and vocal cords. Involuntary movements include:

- **athetosis** – slow writhing movements, particularly in the wrists, fingers and face
- **chorea** – rapid, jerky movements of the head, neck, arms or legs
- **dystonia** – slow, rhythmic movements of the trunk or an entire limb; dystonia may also involve contrived-looking postures, such as severe rotation of the trunk
- **dyskinesia** – literally meaning 'difficulty with movement', dyskinesia is a general term used when the exact type of involuntary movement is difficult to classify.

About 25 per cent of people with cerebral palsy have this athetoid type; it is a result of the middle part of the brain (the basal ganglia) not working properly (see Figure 3.8).

Ataxic cerebral palsy

This condition is characterised by:

- an inability to achieve balance or awkwardness in maintaining it
- a lack of gross and/or fine motor coordination
- a gait which is often high-stepping or lurching
- nystagmus – a rapid, rhythmic, involuntary movement of the eyeball.

Between about 1 and 10 per cent of people with cerebral palsy have this type; it is a result of the cerebellum (which is at the base of the brain) not working properly (see Figure 3.8).

The effects of cerebral palsy

A person with cerebral palsy may have some or most of the following features, in varying degrees of severity:

- slow, awkward or jerky movements
- stiffness
- weakness
- muscle spasms
- floppiness
- unwanted (involuntary) movements

Eyesight

The most common eye problem is a squint which may need correction with glasses or, in severe cases, an operation. Some people may have a cortical vision defect (see page 90), where the part of the brain that is responsible for understanding the images the child sees is not working properly.

Spatial perception

Some people with cerebral palsy find it difficult to judge distances or to think spatially (e.g. to visualise a three-dimensional building). This is due to an abnormality in a part of the brain and is not related to intelligence.

Hearing

People with athetoid cerebral palsy are more likely to have severe hearing difficulties than other children, but the development of 'glue ear' (see page 94) is as likely in a child with any type of cerebral palsy as in unaffected children.

Speech

Speech depends on the ability to control tiny muscles in the mouth, tongue, palate and voice box. Speech difficulties and problems with chewing and swallowing often occur together in people with cerebral palsy.

Epilepsy

Epilepsy (or abnormal electrical discharge from the brain, causing seizures) affects about one in three people with cerebral palsy (see page 69).

Learning ability

Some people with cerebral palsy do have learning difficulties, but this is by no means always the case. Some have higher than average intelligence and some have average intelligence. Some people have difficulty in learning to do certain tasks, e.g. reading, drawing or arithmetic, because a particular part of the brain is affected; it is then termed a 'specific learning difficulty' and should not be confused with the person's general intelligence.

Other difficulties

Some people with cerebral palsy may experience the following difficulties:

- a tendency to chest infections
- constipation
- difficulty in controlling body temperature
- low weight

- frustration leading to behavioural difficulties
- sleep difficulties

Care of people with cerebral palsy

There is no cure for cerebral palsy. It is a non-progressive condition; that is, it does not become more severe as the child gets older, but some difficulties may become more noticeable. If children are lifted, held and positioned well from an early age, and encouraged to play in a way that helps them to improve their posture and muscle control, they can learn a lot and lead fulfilling lives. Physiotherapy is important as it helps with all problems associated with movement. Natural methods such as exercise, manipulation, heat and massage are all used to help the child develop good patterns of movement.

Many parents whose children have cerebral palsy seek new ways of improving their progress through education. Three such programmes are:

- **conductive education** – this has the backing of the charity SCOPE
- **Doman-Delacato therapy** – based on the theory that the brain, like a muscle, will grow if given regular exercise
- **Bobath therapy** – specialised physiotherapy for children with cerebral palsy.

CASE STUDY

Kevin

Kevin has cerebral palsy. When he was about four months old, his parents noticed that he often held his right arm pressed against his body with the fist clenched tightly. He did not sit unaided until he was thirteen months old and now, at age four, is unable to walk without difficulty. He wears splints on his legs which help him to maintain his balance, but he tends to walk jerkily.

Kevin is a lively, intelligent boy who attends a local playgroup three mornings a week and gets on well with the other children there. He becomes frustrated when other children are playing football or using the playground equipment and he cannot join in.

activity

SCOPE (formerly The Spastics Society) is the largest charity working with people who have cerebral palsy, their families and their carers. They produce a number of fact sheets on education and therapy for people with cerebral palsy. If you send off for any fact sheets, remember to enclose a stamped addressed envelope (see 'Useful addresses', page 213).

1 Find out the principles behind (a) conductive education; (b) Bobath therapy; and (c) Doman-Delactao therapy. Where can parents go to have their child assessed? How can Kevin (see case study) be helped to reach his full potential, both now and when he moves to primary school?

2 In groups, design a poster which explains the different types of cerebral palsy and how each type affects the individual.

Disability through illness or accident

Illness and accident are the main causes of disability occurring in those born with no disability. Road traffic accidents (RTAs) are the most common cause of accidents causing disability.

SPINAL CORD INJURY

In the UK, 40,000 people have spinal cord injury as a result of accidents. The single most common cause of spinal cord injury is road traffic accidents. A further 400,000 have damaged spinal cords through illnesses such as:

- spina bifida
- poliomyelitis
- motor neurone disease
- malignant tumours (cancer)
- multiple sclerosis.

Or from conditions affecting the brain, including:

- Parkinson's disease
- brain tumours
- cerebral palsy.

Spinal cord injury prevents messages from the brain from being transmitted down through the spine to the limbs. The injury can be at different levels and cause varying degrees of paralysis:

- **Tetraplegia** means that the damage (or lesion) to the spinal cord was at the cervical level (see Figure 3.6). This results in paralysis of the upper part of the body, including the arms and hands, as well as paralysis of the lower part of the body. Tetraplegia is sometimes called quadriplegia.
- **Paraplegia** arises from damage to the spinal cord at the thoracic or lumbar level, involving paralysis of the lower part of the body. Function and sensation can be affected from the chest down, again depending on the level of the injury and on the extent of the damage.

Paralysis also affects the bladder and bowels, making incontinence a major part of disability. Sometimes the damage is total, resulting in complete loss of feeling and function below the level of the injury. At other times the damage is partial – or 'incomplete' – resulting in incomplete feeling and/or function.

Traumatic injury usually requires eight

to ten weeks lying flat on one's back while the vertebrae stabilise to prevent further damage to the spinal cord. Sometimes surgery is carried out (involving grafting bone on to the damaged vertebrae or the insertion of a metal plate). Once this initial phase is over, the period of *rehabilitation* begins. This usually involves:

- intensive physiotherapy – muscle-building exercises, restoration of balance, etc.
- occupational therapy

- education on the prevention of pressure sores
- education on living with incontinence
- arranging suitable housing
- addressing sexual and relationship needs
- counselling to help with the emotional upheaval.

The following case study highlights the problems faced by anyone who has a disorder which affects both mobility and independence.

CASE STUDY

Independent living

Roger is 47 and a former secondary school teacher who was diagnosed as having cancer of the spine at the age of 28. He had several operations to remove the tumour, but it has left him paralysed in both hands and legs. While the paralysis of his legs is total, Roger retains some function in his hands. His breathing, normal skin sensation, bowel and bladder functions are also affected.

Roger's day begins between 8 and 9 a.m. when the district nurse arrives at his one-bedroom ground floor flat. He lets her in by means of an automatic computerised control system that was installed by social services to help Roger operate various appliances around the house. Thus, he can answer the telephone and front door, or switch on his television, heater and lights simply by pressing a touch pad next to his pillow. Before the nurse has arrived, Roger has already used the system to open the curtains and turn on the radio.

Once she has gained entry, the nurse helps Roger with his personal needs. He is unable to empty his bladder without assistance and so, each morning, it is emptied by inserting a catheter (see page 155). The nurse then applies a penile self-adhesive sheath and drainage bag to collect the urine that he will pass during the course of the day. The same regular attention is given to emptying his bowels, although this is only done twice a week and at the time when Roger showers in his specially adapted bathroom.

Getting washed and dressed is another daily activity with which Roger requires the nurse's help. Because of his paralysis and an inability to sense heat or pressure over most of his body, she must check for signs of **pressure sores** and adjust his shoes and clothing so that they keep him warm, don't cause unnecessary harm to the skin and don't restrict his movement. She also helps him to put on leg calipers (see Chapter 5) and a reinforced bodybrace that improve his balance and sitting position. Once this has been done, the nurse makes a final check of the urinary drainage system before leaving Roger to busy himself with other routine tasks.

These usually begin with the preparation of a light breakfast. His kitchen has lowered work surfaces and is fitted with appliances that he can operate from his wheelchair. However, a wish not to have too many gadgets and to do as much for himself as he can, means that Roger only makes very simple convenience meals which don't always provide him with a full, nutritionally balanced diet.

His wish to be self-reliant also extends to Roger doing all his own shopping, and here he is enormously dependent upon having his own means of transport. Although he receives some **statutory** benefits, Roger decided that his freedom to come and go as he pleased was very important, and so he used his savings to buy an outdoor electric wheelchair and a specially adapted car. The vehicle's automatic ramp and hand steering controls enable him to drive from the wheelchair and to have the type of flexibility and independence that he feels local public or voluntary transport services could not offer him.

Having his own transport has also helped Roger to develop and maintain a busy schedule of other activities. Each week, he spends time managing a helpline for disabled people and attending the regular meetings of several local committees and advisory groups. He also used his car to attend a two-year college course and now conducts weekly counselling sessions for people who, like himself, have a spinal cord injury. These activities have given Roger outside interests as well as focusing his time and energies on things he considers worthwhile.

Roger's social life also offers a change from the domestic routine. He likes eating out, watching rugby and going to the theatre. However, poor wheelchair access and the limitations of the 'back-to-bed' evening nursing service mean that he has to plan ahead and confine his outings to places which have facilities for disabled people. He is also aware that his own inhibitions, as well as other people's prejudices and assumptions about disability, can be a barrier to making new friends and forming long-term relationships.

Being independent and in control are important to Roger and he has taken a great deal of time and effort to negotiate and to secure a package of care that reflects his needs. He recognises that his general physical and emotional well-being, ability to communicate and level of income have helped him to achieve this; although he is also aware that the overall quality of his life is influenced by social and institutional barriers that restrict *all* disabled people and over which he has only limited personal control.

activity

Read the case study above.

1 Identify and list Roger's needs using 'the activities of daily living' (see page 12).
2 How are Roger's daily needs met at the moment?

3 What needs, if any, do you think are not being adequately met?
4 List the delivery of care under two headings – statutory and voluntary
5 What do you think contributes most to Roger's quality of life?

STROKE (CEREBROVASCULAR ACCIDENT OR CVA)

In this condition, the blood supply to part of the brain is suddenly and seriously damaged by a blood clot or a ruptured artery. Strokes are more common in later life and in people who suffer from high blood pressure (**hypertension**). The effect of a stroke depends on how much damage has occurred and which part of the brain is affected. Some common symptoms are:

- a confused emotional state that might be mistaken for drunkenness
- a sudden severe headache
- being unable to move a limb or limbs on one side of the body
- sudden or progressive loss of consciousness
- pupils of the eyes are unequal in size
- loss of bladder or bowel control (incontinence).

CASE STUDY

The effects of a stroke (CVA)

Peter Hodges is 65 years old and lives with his wife, Jean, in a small council-owned house. Until one year ago, Peter worked as a postman in a large town in the Midlands. He had joined the Royal Mail at the age of 16 and was looking forward to retiring at the statutory retirement age of 65. However, one year ago Peter collapsed suddenly while working on his allotment. He was rushed to hospital and it was found that he had suffered a stroke. He now has a left **hemiplegia** – paralysis of both limbs on the left side of the body –

and **dysarthria** – difficulty in articulating speech.

Jean had always worked as a shop assistant in the local greengrocer's but has had to give up her job in order to look after Peter. The Hodges have no children but are popular members of their community and still take an interest in the local church. Jean is not able to help Peter meet all his needs, but wants to do as much as she can and is very grateful for all the help she receives. Recently, Jean has not been feeling well – she often wakes up feeling tired and depressed, her back aches and she has put on quite a lot of weight since giving up work.

Peter can manage to get around the house by using a tripod walking aid. His speech is greatly improved but he still becomes frustrated at his inability to say what he means to say. He has always been independent and is now worried for Jean's health as she looks so tired all the time. Peter's main hobby is gardening and he misses the companionship of his allotment friends and feels 'cooped up' since they decided to move his bed downstairs.

Peter's package of care includes visits from a district nurse and a home care assistant, and his needs were originally assessed by an occupational therapist. Both Peter and Jean feel they need a holiday as the past two years have been stressful, but they don't know whether going on holiday in itself might be *more* stressful.

activity

1 What are the main problems (a) for Peter and (b) for Jean?
2 How could the quality of their lives be improved?
3 Think of ways in which voluntary organisations could help.
4 Carry out research into strokes (cerebrovascular accidents):
   - What actually happens in the brain during a stroke?
   - What is the frequency of strokes? Are men or women more likely to suffer a stroke and at what age is it likely to occur? Represent your findings on a pie chart or bar graph.
   - Can strokes be prevented and do some lifestyles or activities predispose certain people to experience strokes?

EPILEPSY

Epilepsy is a condition of the nervous system affecting about 1 in 200 people. It is not a mental illness and cannot be 'caught'. A person with epilepsy experiences convulsions, usually called seizures or fits. The seizure is caused by a temporary 'electrical storm' in the brain. Anyone can be affected by epilepsy:

- more than 300,000 people in the UK have epilepsy
- 50 per cent of people affected start under the age of 16 years
- 30 per cent of children with epilepsy find that it disappears by the time they reach adolescence
- it is not an inherited condition, but some of the factors which contribute to it may be inherited.

There are three main types of seizure: partial, generalised absence, and generalised tonic clonic.

Partial

These affect only part of the brain. There are two types:

1 **Complex**: seizures may start with an 'aura' or warning, such as a funny taste

in the mouth, a peculiar sound that the person hears or flashing lights, or there may be no seizure as such, but the person may be unaware of their surroundings and start to make odd lip-smacking noises or pluck at their clothing.

2 **Simple**: seizures may involve some twitching of the body and the person may complain of feeling 'strange'.

There is no loss of consciousness.

Generalised absence

This used to be called 'petit mal' epilepsy and affects the whole brain. There may be:

- sudden 'switching off' in which the person seems to be in a trance
- slight twitching movements of the eyelids, head or mouth
- strange 'automatic' movements such as chewing, making odd noises, fiddling with clothing, etc.

Generalised tonic clonic

This is also known as 'grand mal' epilepsy, and usually follows a pattern:

- the person suddenly falls unconscious, often with a cry (caused by tightening of the voice muscles)
- he or she goes rigid, arching the back (tonic phase)
- breathing may stop and the lips may become cyanosed (tinged with blue, due to lack of oxygen)
- convulsive movements begin (clonic phase); the jaw may be clenched and the breathing noisy
- saliva may appear at the mouth
- bladder or bowel control may be lost
- muscles relax and the breathing becomes normal again.

Consciousness is usually regained within a few minutes; the person may feel dazed or fall into a very deep sleep.

Management of epilepsy

Most seizures can be controlled by taking regular medication, often phenobarbitone. There are many different drugs available, and it sometimes takes time to find out which one is best for each individual. People with epilepsy can play most sports, although it is not advisable to swim alone. People with epilepsy are not allowed to drive a car in the UK unless they have been free from seizures for one year or have an established pattern of sleep seizure only.

If someone has a seizure, take the following first-aid measures:

- If the person is falling, try to ease the fall. Make space around the person and ask bystanders to move away.
- Do not use force to restrain them or put anything in their mouth
- Loosen clothing around their neck and protect their head.
- When the seizures have stopped, place them in the **recovery position** (see Figure 3.9) and stay with them until they have recovered.

You only need to send for an ambulance if:

- it is a first seizure and you don't know why it happened
- it follows a blow to the head
- the person is injured during the seizure
- the seizure is continuous and shows no sign of stopping – a rare condition called *status epilepticus*.

There is a lack of awareness about epilepsy among the general population, probably based on ignorance and misunderstanding of the condition. Epilepsy does not affect intelligence; it rarely, if

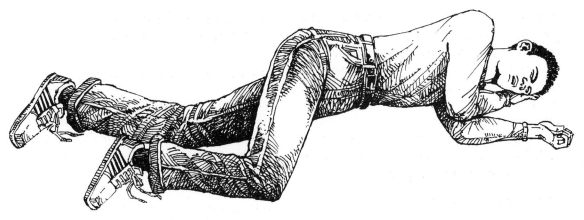

Figure 3.9   The recovery position

ever, causes any learning or behaviour problems unless there is another condition present. Eighty per cent of children with epilepsy attend mainstream schools and most adults with epilepsy are employed.

MULTIPLE SCLEROSIS

Multiple sclerosis (MS), sometimes referred to as disseminated sclerosis, is a degenerative disorder which affects the brain and the spinal cord, which are together known as the central nervous system (CNS). The damage to the CNS in this condition occurs in many widely scattered places (multiple = many), and the damaged area is filled with hard material or scars (sclerosis = scars).

MS is the most common acquired (i.e. non-congenital) disorder of the nervous system in young adults. It is a disorder largely found in temperate countries where the incidence is approximately one in every 1,000 people. Women are more likely to acquire MS than men in a ratio of 3 : 2.

Characteristics of multiple sclerosis

The course and severity of the disorder vary considerably from one person to another, but is usually slowly progressive. There may be alternating periods of *remissions* (when symptoms are mild or absent) and *relapses* (when symptoms are present and often severe in effect); however, some people with MS do not experience this pattern of alternating remissions and relapses. Areas affected are:

- **Movement**: damage to the spinal cord may lead to tingling, numbness or a feeling of constriction in any part of the body. Arms and legs may feel heavy and become weak. Spasticity (increased rigidity) and paralysis sometimes develop.
- **Sensation**: when the sensory nerve fibres are involved, there may be areas of numbness or pins and needles in the skin. Hands and feet tend to feel cold.
- **Coordination**: if the nerve fibres in the brain stem are affected, there may be loss of balance and loss of coordination.
- **Vision**: this may become blurred; there may also be double vision or *nystagmus*

(involuntary movement of the eyes from side to side).

- **Continence**: if the spinal cord is badly damaged, urinary incontinence develops due to loss of **sphincter** control in the bladder.
- **Emotions**: mood changes are common; there may be depression or euphoria, or both.
- **Fatigue**: most people with MS experience overwhelming tiredness at times and general fatigue.

Many people with MS find that the emotional and psychological problems that go with having the disorder – such as poor self-image, grief and mourning for the loss of the old self – are more difficult to come to terms with than the physical effects.

Diagnosis

There is no single diagnostic test for MS. The following investigations may be carried out to exclude other disorders and so arrive at a correct diagnosis:

- **Lumbar puncture**: a sample of cerebrospinal fluid (CSF) is removed from the spinal canal for laboratory analysis.
- **CT scan**: this technique uses X-rays to measure variations in the density of the organs being examined; it compiles a picture by computer analysis.
- **Magnetic Resonance Imaging (MRI)**: this technique produces images which are similar to, and in certain parts of the body (including the brain and spinal cord) superior to those of the CT scanner, but without the radiation hazard.

Causes

The cause of MS is not known, but there are many theories, including:

- **Auto-immune disorder**: the body's defence system begins to treat the myelin sheath (which protects the nerve fibres) as foreign tissue, and so destroys it.
- **A genetic factor**: relatives of affected people are eight times more likely than others to contract the disorder.
- **Environmental factors**: MS is five times more prevalent in temperate zones (e.g. Europe and the USA) than in the tropics.
- **Viral**: an unidentified virus may be contracted by a susceptible person and later give rise to MS.

Treatment

As yet, there is no known cure or specific treatment for MS, although recently researchers have been looking into the effectiveness and practicalities of *myelin transplantation*. In the USA, trials are currently under way for a drug called Beta-interferon-id.

Guidelines for management of MS

- Eat a healthy, low-fat diet.
- Supplement the diet with essential fatty acids (e.g. evening primrose oil) plus vitamins and minerals.
- Take daily exercise and physiotherapy.
- Maintain a positive attitude to life.
- Keep the brain active and stimulated.
- Get enough rest.
- Avoid fatigue.
- Have satisfying relationships with other people.
- Lead a stress-free life.
- Try hyperbaric oxygen treatment – a method of increasing the amount of oxygen in the tissues by placing the person in a special chamber where oxygen is pumped at up to three times normal atmospheric pressure.

CASE STUDY

Stolen feelings

Andrew Gregan went from being a doctor to a patient when he contracted multiple sclerosis. Here he talks of that traumatic change.

'I woke up one Friday morning in April 1994 not knowing that the pins and needles I was feeling in my toes would signal the start of the rest of my life. I was 29 years old, a junior doctor who was anxious not to take time off work. I brushed it off as just another viral illness. By Monday, the sensation was up to my chest and when I bent my neck I felt a shock wave down my spine.

The diagnosis of multiple sclerosis was as swift and unheralded as the onset of the symptoms. I sat facing the neurologist alone. No one of note in my life was present. There was no fanfare of trumpets to announce the diagnosis: I could have been diagnosed as having flu. I dealt with each relapse and the disabilities it brought by trusting in my medical education that I would soon have a remission. It didn't happen and it never has. I know that I've been unlucky – most people with MS do not become so disabled, so quickly.

The input I have had from health professionals in the last 18 months would read like a shopping list for an underfunded health authority. It includes three consultant neurologists, one consultant in rehabilitation neurology, one professor of neurology, one consultant ophthalmologist and a consultant urologist.

If results in medicine were dependent on effort, I would be running a marathon. Instead, I sit in a wheelchair longing to walk again. I must plan my days in advance to avoid the embarrassment of being incontinent. Ball sports on TV, subtitled films and small print have been consigned to the past. Blind-spots in both eyes have seen to that. From my neck down I have pins and needles and my fingertips are numb. I am cocooned in an unfeeling world with just my head jutting out to remind me that touch is a wonderful and undervalued sense. Multiple sclerosis doesn't just disable its victims – it steals your energy. This can be one of the hardest things to get across to able-bodied people, who can appreciate the physical disabilities, but interpret an unwillingness to participate in the most sedate activity as apathy and a sign of depression.

The most soul-destroying feature of MS is its progressive nature. As you adapt to a new disability, compensating for its physical restrictions and reinforcing your mental strength, you are constantly aware that the next day can bring a new one. If you break your leg or have an operation your family and friends are invariably prominent in their support. Relationships don't change, friends don't suddenly take flight and families don't go into denial. Develop a chronic illness and the cards, flowers and visitors can be underwhelming. Some of my friends and family couldn't cope. The medical profession,

contd. ▌▌▌➡

despite accusations of being a closed shop, has often shown me bad manners and a closed door.

My wife is one of the things in my life worth fighting for – we got married last year knowing I had MS. We have experienced extremes of emotion that we might not have done if we had lived 10 lifetimes free of disability. Self-image and self-worth are often overlooked when faced with disabilities in MS. I have found it a huge burden to go from being a doctor with a positive image in society to a disabled person. I tell myself that I am winning in my struggle. Conceitedly, I tell myself that I know of no one else who would have coped. Every morning begins with a roll call of function. Can I swallow? What can I see? What can I feel? Can I speak? Have I soiled the bed? What can I move? This harrowing routine is not lessened by familiarity. I stretch my legs and back for half an hour, three times a day, to try to relieve the muscle spasm. After a strip-wash I contemplate another day of inactivity.

Like any person, I want to work. A computer-based or academic job are the only areas that are feasible. Since I, with a medical degree, cannot find work in these areas, then what hope is there for the wheelchair-bound MS sufferer whose skills were originally manual?

It sounds hard and it is. But that doesn't mean there is no hope. There are over a dozen drugs undergoing trials at the moment. So far, only one, Beta-interferon-id has been licensed for use in MS. In America, tens of thousands of sufferers have been taking it for two years or more. In Britain, the guidelines for prescribing this drug are strict – partly because of cost. The holy grail for MS sufferers is the prospect of myelin transplantation (myelin is the insulating sheath around the nerves that is lost in MS). Giant steps have been made in this area in the last few years. All research must, however, be subject to peer review (process where it is examined by other experts) because questionable results can give false hope and divert funding from proven treatments.

I am told I can expect to live another 40 years or more. With no immediate prospect of improvement and a very real prospect that things will get worse, I can only see my future in terms of a cure.'

(*The Guardian*, 4/6/1996)

activity

Read the case study above.

1 List the problems that Andrew found to be the hardest to overcome.
2 Draw up a list of specific needs using the activities of daily living model described on page 12.
3 Find out about complementary therapies. Are there any particular areas of complementary medicine that could be useful in combating some of the disabilities caused by multiple sclerosis?

Chronic illness

Under the broad definition of 'special needs', people suffering from a chronic illness may require specialist services on a regular basis in the same way that a person with a physical disability requires assistance. Strauss (1984) states that chronic illness has the following characteristics:

- it is permanent
- it leaves residual disability
- it is non-reversible
- it requires special training of the patient for rehabilitation
- it is likely to require a long period of supervision, observation or care.

Chronic disorders are usually contrasted with acute ones (of sudden onset and of short duration). A person with a chronic illness shows little change in symptoms from day to day and may be able, with some difficulty, to carry out normal daily activities. The disease process is continuous with progressive deterioration, sometimes in spite of treatment. The person may experience an acute exacerbation (flare-up) of symptoms.

Some examples of chronic illness in children are:

- juvenile rheumatoid arthritis
- chronic renal failure
- psoriasis – skin disorder
- atopic eczema
- juvenile diabetes mellitus
- sickle cell disease (see page 50)
- thalassaemia major (see page 52)
- asthma.

Some examples of chronic illness in adults are:

- Crohn's disease
- rheumatoid arthritis
- leukaemia
- ischaemic heart disease
- motor neurone disease (MND)
- myasthenia gravis
- drug dependence
- ulcerative colitis
- osteoarthritis
- incontinence
- emphysema
- psoriasis
- ankylosing spondylitis
- diabetes mellitus.

It is estimated that, at any given time, around half the general population has a chronic disorder which requires medical management. These disorders range from mild conditions such as partial hearing loss to serious life-threatening conditions such as renal failure and heart disease.

Certain specific needs arise from chronic illness; these are summarised in Figure 3.10.

Long-term illness may mean that the person's ability to exercise freedom of choice in daily activities is curtailed. Frequent periods of hospitalisation disrupt family and social life and impose strain on all members of the family. When a child has a chronic illness, siblings often resent the extra attention given to the sick child and parents may also need financial support. Social workers based at hospitals will give advice on any benefits (see Chapter 5) and can provide a counselling service. They may also be able to put parents in touch with an organisation for parents of children with similar conditions.

The majority of people suffering from chronic illnesses are able to manage without help from another person and do not

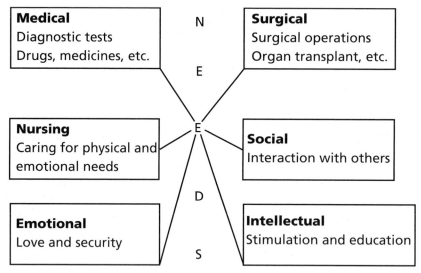

Figure 3.10   A summary of the special needs of people with chronic illness

have any significant mobility problems. As the diseases are normally confined to adults, even those with persistent symptoms are usually able to look after themselves.

CHRONIC OBSTRUCTIVE AIRWAYS DISEASE

Chronic obstructive airways disease (COAD) is a term used to describe a condition in which there is irreversible and usually progressive limitation of airflow into and out of the lungs. Both *chronic bronchitis* and *emphysema* come within this definition.

The main symptoms arising from these conditions are:

- breathlessness
- swelling of the feet and ankles, because of fluid retention

- chest pain.

Complications are heart failure and, in advanced cases, reduced oxygen supply to the brain which may lead to confusion and disturbances of consciousness.

Care needs

Only in advanced disease will a person with COAD require help with any of the daily living skills (see page 12). When the person is effectively bed-bound because the slightest exertion causes severe symptoms, then help is required in areas such as dressing, washing and preparing meals. The person may also need oxygen therapy via a portable cylinder in the home (the administration of supplementary oxygen for the purpose of preventing the damage to tissue cells caused by lack of oxygen).

activity

Choose one of the chronic illnesses mentioned on page 75 to research.

1 Prepare a short (5–10 minutes) presentation to the rest of your group or class, to include the following points:
   - a brief description of the illness
   - who is most likely to suffer from it
   - how it is diagnosed and treated
   - what special needs the person with the illness may have
   - who the carers in the community are

and what equipment and services may be needed.

2 Evaluate each other's presentation, having agreed on the criteria beforehand with your teacher/tutor.

Certain cancers and accidents will result in restrictions to mobility and other abilities. Many disorders which have different origins or causes will result in very similar problems in practical terms.

PARKINSON'S DISEASE

Parkinson's disease is characterised by a collection of signs involving the nervous system. The main effect is a lack of an essential chemical transmitter, *dopamine*, which can be effectively replaced by modern drug therapy. Parkinson's disease can affect people from all races and social classes, and men and women are equally affected. The illness is more common in elderly people. It is caused by the degeneration of pigmented nerve cells in the brain. It seldom shortens life expectancy to any significant degree. About 1 person in 200 has Parkinson's disease.

Features of Parkinson's disease

Symptoms vary a great deal from one person to another. The main symptoms of Parkinson's disease are:

- **Tremor**: the commonest early symptom is shaking (tremor) of one or both hands. It occurs at rest and is reduced or stopped when the limb is in active movement. It usually disappears during sleep.
- **Rigidity**: there is often stiffness and a sense of effort required to move the limb, which may feel heavy and weak.
- **Akinesia**: this means a lack of spontaneous movement. **Bradykinesia**, or slowness in starting a movement or slowness during the movement, is also common.
- **Micrographia**: the handwriting becomes progressively smaller and may show the characteristic tremor (micro = small, graphos = writing).
- **Disorders of posture**: these refer to the bent position of the neck and trunk; the arms are held close to the sides, elbows and wrists slightly bent. Such posture develops late in the course of the illness.
- **Loss of balance**: this often accompanies disorders of posture. The person finds it difficult to correct a trip or a stumble; a shuffling, unbalanced walk may break into uncontrollable, tiny, running steps called *festination* (from the Latin *festinare* = to hurry).

Other commonly experienced symptoms include an unblinking, fixed facial expression, changed bladder and bowel habits and difficulty in swallowing.

Diagnosis

There are no specific diagnostic tests to confirm Parkinson's disease. A definite diagnosis is usually made by a neurologist, based on the history and signs offered by the patient.

Treatment

There is as yet no medical cure for Parkinson's disease. Treatment is aimed at eliminating as far as possible, the symptoms and disabilities caused by the illness; with such an aim in mind, treatment is tailor-made to suit the needs of each individual and requires adjustments at intervals over the entire course of the disease. Various drugs are used in the later stages of the illness: these include dopamines, which replace the essential chemicals lacking in the brain. Surgical treatment is undergoing trials but is rarely recommended.

Management of Parkinson's disease

The first step to managing the symptoms is to identify them; the following methods are used.

Physiotherapy

Assessment of the individual is made by a trained physiotherapist. This includes:

- the physical disabilities
- learning capacity and mental state
- home circumstances – the availability of able-bodied friends and family to continue to practise any instructions.

Exercises and activities are planned to correct abnormal gait and bad posture, to prevent or minimise stiffness of the joints and to provide a routine which can be practised at home by the patient.

Occupational therapy

A home visit by an occupational therapist identifies specific problems, the need for hand rails, high seats and other appliances.

Speech therapy

For those who find that their speech is monotonous, slow or hesitant, speech therapy can offer a method of retraining, using *audio feedback*. This enables the patient to hear his or her own speech after a measured interval and to learn how to improve both voice and speech output. Other aids to communication include:

- **Edu-Com scanning** – a device which points to a word or picture showing the person's intention and meaning
- **Micro-writer** – a device that links a TV, printer or speech synthesiser and can sometimes help when speech training is unsuccessful
- **Personal computer (PC)** – this is often invaluable in the writing of letters and in performing business activities at home.

MEETING PHYSICALLY DISABLED PEOPLE

When talking for more than a few minutes to someone in a wheelchair, try to put yourself at their eye level to avoid stiff necks.

Check the following:

- Are there suitable parking arrangements?
- Is there a step-free or ramped entrance?

- Are there suitable toilet facilities?
- Is there a lift if required?
- Is reception alerted to provide assistance?

- If there are potential access problems, notify the person in advance and discuss what can be done.

Stress-related illness

Stress and how we manage our own stress levels has a direct link to our general well-being. Various illnesses may be said to be either caused or triggered by stress, including:

- stomach ulcers
- skin disorders, e.g. eczema and psoriasis
- heart attacks
- myalgic encephalomyelitis (ME).

MYALGIC ENCEPHALOMYELITIS (ME)

ME is sometimes called post-viral fatigue syndrome. It affects around 150,000 people in the UK and people in the caring professions make up the largest group affected, with three times as many women as men. No one definite cause is known, but theories have suggested the following:

- persistent viral infection
- damage to the immune system following a viral infection
- a neurotic disorder, e.g. hyperventilation ('overbreathing').

The main features of ME are:

- muscle fatigue
- headaches
- muscular pains
- depression
- exhaustion
- dizziness
- fever
- bowel and digestive problems.

There are no diagnostic tests, although enteroviruses can be traced in the colon of more than half of people with ME. Diagnosis is by process of elimination of other illnesses and disorders. The medical profession has little to offer in terms of scientific explanation or treatment of ME. The following treatments are among the more common:

- anti-depressants are often prescribed but their long-term use is not recommended
- a diet that is sugar-free and yeast-free; stress is thought to lead to an impaired immune system in which yeast infections (e.g. Candida albicans or thrush) can flourish
- relaxation techniques such as the Alexander technique, meditation and yoga
- homoeopathy
- acupuncture
- herbal treatments with, for example, evening primrose oil
- counselling.

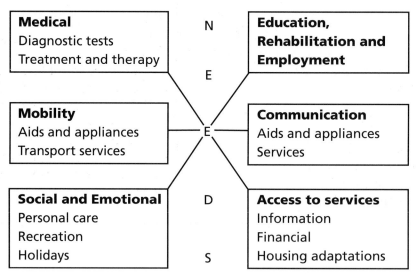

Figure 3.11 A summary of the special needs of physically disabled people

CASE STUDY

ME

Before becoming ill with ME, Debbie, aged 33, had led an active life both at work as a midwife and outside her job, having many interests which occupied most of her spare time. In particular, Debbie liked scuba diving and going to her local gym. She made little time for relaxation and her diet was high in sugar and carbohydrates. Her emotional history had been stressful. She had had several boyfriends, and at one point had considered marrying one of them. Then he had been sent overseas by his firm and she later found out that he had married someone else within months of leaving the UK.

When she became ill, she suffered from most of the common symptoms of ME and was bedridden for three months. After numerous setbacks and relapses, she is now in the fifth year of her illness and has tried diet, homoeopathy, herbal treatments and counselling as her path to recovery. The most difficult experiences for Debbie were the financial implications of being ill. She lost her job and has been living on state benefits. She has found her practical circumstances difficult to reconcile with her need for relaxation and a reduction in stress. After five years out of work it will be hard for her to find a job, particularly with this history of ill-health. She says that counselling has empowered her to face the stresses and difficulties which the future might hold, without becoming ill again. However, the whole experience has left her feeling bitter and resentful of a system which seems to deny her experiences as having any validity.

activity

Read Debbie's story, then answer the following questions:

1 What are the signs and symptoms of long-term stress?
2 What advice and recommendations should be made to a person who shows all the symptoms of stress, to avoid them contracting ME?
3 What support should be made available to people with ME by (a) the NHS; (b) the DSS; (c) the workplace; and (d) friends and family.
4 Many people with ME feel isolated as there is still a lot of ignorance about the condition. How could this be combated?

Life-threatening illness

Today, with good medical and nursing care, many deaths, even those from cancer, are pain-free and are associated with little physical discomfort. The two most obvious responses to the onset of a chronic or terminal disorder are *anxiety* and *depression*. Uncertainty about the illness and about what will happen is one of the most likely causes of such anxiety and depression.

WHAT IS CANCER?

Cancer is the term applied to a group of neoplastic (literally meaning new growth) diseases in which normal body cells are changed into malignant ones. Normally the cells of tissues are regularly replaced by new growth which stops when old cells have been replaced. In cancer, this cell growth is unregulated. The cells continue to grow even after the repair of damaged tissue is complete. The malignant cells multiply and invade neighbouring tissues, thereby destroying the normal cells and taking their place. If the lymphatic cells are invaded, the malignant cells are carried away in the lymph until their progress is halted by the filtering effect of the lymph glands. Here, they may be deposited and cause a secondary tumour (also called a *metastasis*). Malignant disease is progressive and, untreated, results in death in most cases. Even with treatment most people still die from the effects of their cancer, although certain tumours are now very responsive to treatment. In particular, treatment of *leukaemia* and *lymphoma* is now so successful that many people are considered to have been cured.

LEUKAEMIA

In leukaemia, abnormally growing white blood cells are scattered throughout the bone marrow, rather than grouped into a single tumour. Leukaemia is the most common form of childhood cancer. The age of onset is most likely around five years. Symptoms include:

- bleeding from the gums – due to insufficient production of platelet cells needed to stop bleeding
- headache – due to anaemia
- epistaxis – nosebleeds
- enlarged **lymph nodes** – in the neck, armpit and groin
- anaemia – causing tiredness, breathlessness on exertion and pallor
- bone and joint pain – due to abnormality of the bone marrow
- frequent bruising – due to reduced platelet production
- infections – the immature white cells are unable to resist infections, e.g. chest or throat infections, **herpes zoster** or skin infections.

Diagnosis

Diagnosis of acute leukaemia is based on a bone marrow biopsy that confirms an abnormal number of immature white blood cells (blasts).

Treatment

- Blood and platelet transfusions
- Anti-cancer drugs
- Radiotherapy – treatment by X-rays
- Bone marrow transplantation
- **Protective isolation nursing** (reverse barrier nursing)

Treatment is often successful: 75 per cent of children with the commonest form of leukaemia are well five years after diagnosis.

Side-effects of cancer treatment

Some anti-cancer treatments have distressing side-effects:

- **Sudden hair loss**: wigs are provided for children who lose their hair during treatment, but they should not be forced to wear them if it makes them feel uncomfortable.
- **Nausea and vomiting**: the child will need a great deal of support to cope with these acute symptoms during treatment.
- **Change in body shape**: some corticosteroid drugs cause the young patient to develop a characteristic 'moon face' and a build-up of fatty tissue.

It is difficult for parents to appreciate the benefits of treatment which causes such distressing side-effects when they are grieving and trying to adjust to the diagnosis of the illness. The treatment can seem more unpleasant than the effects of the illness it is trying to fight. Children with cancer – the most common life-threatening disease – number 1 in 600. Chemotherapy (treatment by drugs) and radiotherapy (treatment by deep X-rays) have altered the course of the disease and can sometimes effect a complete cure.

Support for the child and family

There are many professionals who can offer help and support for the child and family going through the trauma of terminal illness.

In the hospital, there are:

- nurses
- doctors
- social workers
- play therapists
- bereavement counsellors
- representatives of different religious bodies.

In the community, there are:

- Macmillan nurses – trained district nurses who specialise in visiting people with terminal illness
- in some areas, Hospital at Home services which enable sick patients to

receive 24 hour nursing care in their own homes
- the primary health care team – GP, district nurse, health visitor, practice nurse
- voluntary support groups.

HIV INFECTION AND AIDS

- HIV stands for human immunodeficiency virus.
- AIDS stands for acquired immune deficiency syndrome.
- The HIV virus has been identified as the cause of AIDS.

The HIV virus was identified in 1983 as an RNA virus of the type known as retroviruses. The disease known as AIDS was first noticed among homosexual men in New York and California in 1981. It has received enormous publicity worldwide because it is a disease affecting relatively young people and is, at present, usually fatal. The genetic blueprint of most viruses is stored in the form of the chemical DNA. Retroviruses differ from this pattern, however, since their genetic material is stored in the form of a related but different chemical called RNA. One sub-family of the retroviruses is known to cause leukaemia in humans, but the sub-family to which HIV belongs was previously only known to cause fatal diseases in sheep, horses and goats. HIV affects the immune system, replicating in a particular type of lymphocyte called the T4 cell. T4 cells or 'helper' cells induce other T-cells to fight invading organisms. Without them the body's immune system breaks down, leaving the patient exposed to a variety of diseases.

It is important to realise that infection with HIV does not necessarily result in AIDS. Some people are carriers of the disease while remaining symptom-free. The disease has been discovered too recently to know whether all people with HIV will eventually have AIDS.

How is HIV transmitted?

HIV is passed from one person to another:

- during unprotected penetrative sex
- by sharing needles and syringes used for injecting drugs
- by transfer of blood, blood products or organs
- from mother to baby across the placenta during birth and via breast milk.

The virus cannot survive outside the body (unlike the flu virus, for example) and is destroyed by acid in the stomach.

Signs and symptoms

The first signs and symptoms are a short flu-like illness, followed by no signs or symptoms for months or years. The incubation period is normally six weeks to several months, but may extend for years. Because of a defect in the immune response, other opportunistic infections follow (see Figure 3.12).

Treatment

There is no known cure for AIDS. Antibiotics may be prescribed to treat symptoms such as pneumonia, and radiotherapy used to treat the various cancers, but these treatments do not constitute a cure. Research is aimed at developing a drug to inactivate the virus and/or a vaccine to provide immunity to HIV. Until such measures are found, prevention is the most effective method of controlling the spread of AIDS.

Prevention

- Reduce the number of sexual partners.

Symptoms of AIDS

AIDS is a 'syndrome' and causes a number of different diseases. It can make people lose weight very quickly and feel as though they have very little energy.

It can give them headaches and fevers, often at night, and make them weak and ill, especially in the later stages.

HIV can cause skin diseases. People sometimes find purple patches on their skin. This is a symptom of Kaposi's sarcoma, a cancer that affects many AIDS patients. It is not usually painful.

More painful are cold sores, which are caused by a virus and are found on the face, neck, mouth and glands.

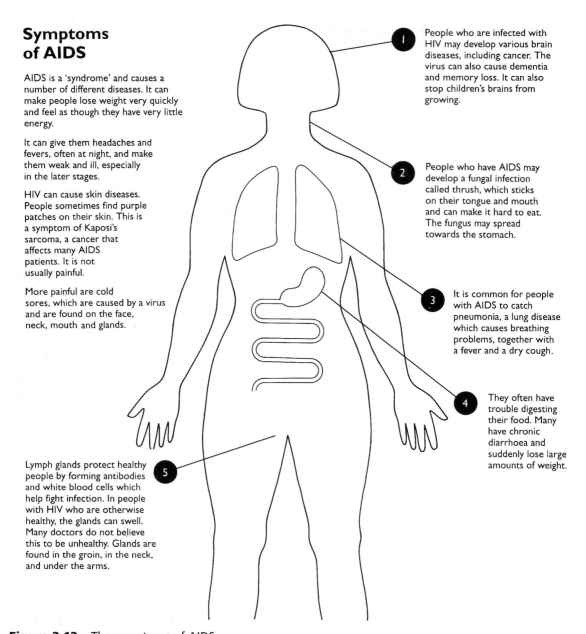

1. People who are infected with HIV may develop various brain diseases, including cancer. The virus can also cause dementia and memory loss. It can also stop children's brains from growing.

2. People who have AIDS may develop a fungal infection called thrush, which sticks on their tongue and mouth and can make it hard to eat. The fungus may spread towards the stomach.

3. It is common for people with AIDS to catch pneumonia, a lung disease which causes breathing problems, together with a fever and a dry cough.

4. They often have trouble digesting their food. Many have chronic diarrhoea and suddenly lose large amounts of weight.

5. Lymph glands protect healthy people by forming antibodies and white blood cells which help fight infection. In people with HIV who are otherwise healthy, the glands can swell. Many doctors do not believe this to be unhealthy. Glands are found in the groin, in the neck, and under the arms.

Figure 3.12   The symptoms of AIDS

- Ideally, sex should be restricted to partners whose sexual history is known.
- Use of a condom is recommended for both anal and vaginal intercourse.
- Intravenous drug users should not share needles or syringes.

Care needs of people with AIDS

There is a lot of fear, ignorance and stigma associated with HIV and AIDS. The care needs will be the same as those for any serious illness. In addition, there are specialist counselling services and buddy programmes for people with 'full-blown' AIDS.

Loss and bereavement

Loss is experienced in a variety of ways, not necessarily involving the death of a loved one; for example, growing up involves loss of infancy support networks; going to school involves temporary separation from parents; changing school involves loss of familiar surroundings and possible peer friendships. Obviously, there are corresponding 'gains' here as well, for example the child gains new friends and experiences with each change in circumstance. Other life events that involve loss are:

- new siblings (loss of parental attention)
- death of a sibling
- bereavement, as grandparents grow older and die
- loss of parent through separation, divorce or death
- ending or changing relationships
- unemployment (parent's, sibling's or one's own)
- miscarriage or stillbirth
- birth of a baby with a disability (parents may grieve for the loss of a 'normal' child)
- disability (loss of a sense of the future and of security)
- caring for people with dementia or Alzheimer's disease (see Chapter 4).

GRIEF

Grief is a normal and necessary response to the death of a loved one. It can be short-lived or last a long time. Grief can take the form of several clearly defined stages (see Table 3.2).

The rate of progress through these stages depends on the individual's temperament and the circumstances of his or her loss. Most people come through the healing process of grief with the help of relatives and friends, but those who have little family support or who have shown suicidal tendencies may require skilled help from outside. Research has shown that counselling can help to reduce the damage to physical and mental health which sometimes follows the loss of a loved one.

BEREAVEMENT COUNSELLING

Bereavement counsellors try to establish a warm, trusting relationship with the bereaved person. This is done initially by listening with patience and sympathy, and by accepting tears as natural and even desirable. Bereavement counselling should not be undertaken by individuals working alone. The support of a group under professional guidance is vital, as close contact with intense grief can be very emotional demanding and stressful.

1 Shock and disbelief	Numbness and withdrawal from others enables the bereaved person to get through the funeral arrangements and family gatherings. This stage may last from three days to three months.
2 Denial	No loss is acknowledged; the bereaved person behaves as if the dead person were still there. Hallucinations are a common experience – these may consist of a sense of having seen or heard the dead person or of having been aware of his or her presence. This stage usually occurs within the first 14 days and can last minutes, hours or weeks.
3 Growing awareness:	Some or all of the following emotions may be felt:
longing	the urge to search, to try to find a reason for the death
anger	directed against any or all of the following: the medical services; the person(s) who caused the death, in case of accident; God for allowing it to happen; the deceased for abandoning them
depression	the pain of the loss is felt, often with feelings of lack of self-worth
guilt	this may be guilt for the real or imagined negligence inflicted on the person who has just died; or the bereaved can feel guilty about his or her own feelings and inability to enjoy life
anxiety	often bordering on panic, as the full impact of the loss is realised. There may be worry about the future, new responsibilities and loneliness. There may even be thoughts of suicide.
4 Acceptance	This usually occurs in the second year, after the death has been relived at the first anniversary. The bereaved person is then able to relearn the world and new situations with all their changes *without* the deceased person.

Table 3.2 The stages of grief

CASE STUDY

Saying goodbye to Ben

The following article was written by a mother whose son died aged three years nine months.

'It is now over four years since Ben was born, and I have lost all sense of time in relation to events. Sometimes it seems only a few weeks since his birth and only yesterday that we were told he wouldn't live to be a year old. Ben had been born with hypertrophic obstructive cardiomyopathy, a heart-muscle disease very rare in children, but inoperable.

Our lives were full of hospital after that, lots of clinic visits, admissions and a long stay for **open heart surgery**. The hospital became like a second home – except it was a home you don't want to go to. The nurses and doctors became good friends – but they were friends you would rather not have to make. One of the most consoling aspects of our stays in hospital was the contact we made with other parents; you form your own support groups, which are very important. Most sick children need to have their mother or father with them for reassurance. Nowadays, most hospitals encourage parents to stay, but it can be exhausting to be there without a break. You long for the day you can leave, but when you are told you can go home, it suddenly seems too soon. You aren't ready to carry the whole responsibility. And when you get home, where is everybody? You have lost not only the nurses and doctors and the support of other hospital parents, but

most of your friends and neighbours, it seems.

People avoid you because they do not know what to say. If only they would simply put their arms around you without saying anything. Instead, parents find themselves landed with the extra burden of having to make it easier for other people, jollying along an awkward phone conversation. You find yourself consoling people who should be consoling you, and who might like to, if they knew how.

One of the hardest things about the whole gruelling business is balancing your life between the child in crisis and the others who need you too. Ben was our fourth child and, though the three others could be amazingly understanding for children of primary school age, they are nevertheless only human and were understandably resentful at times, although they wouldn't have parted with their fragile little brother for anything in the world.

After 19 months of living with Ben and his disease and coping with the trauma of open heart surgery, we had to face the fact that he had deteriorated so much that he now needed a heart transplant. We were lucky; many children never get the chance they deserve and die while on the waiting list. We will always hold a special place in our hearts for a very brave family in France who thought of others in the midst of their tragedy. After the transplant, we had real hope. Ben had a new,

contd. ▌▌▌➡

healthy heart and was growing and developing normally, though he had to take powerful medicines to prevent rejection.

Then, one Thursday in June, 18 months after the operation, Ben became ill. He was admitted to Birmingham Children's Hospital the same evening and transferred to the intensive care unit and put on a ventilator the next day. Although Ben had been very close to death in the past, I had never before experienced the feelings I did now. The memory of that terror and helplessness will never leave me.

He just lay there, the ventilator tube protruding from his nose, wires and tubes connected to his beautiful, perfect little body. Tony and I sat by him, stroking him, holding his hands and kissing his downy skin. I felt as if part of me was being torn away, and I could do nothing but watch and wait. I talked to Ben, though I didn't think he could hear me.

The consultant was with Ben all day and all night and at one point we told him that if Ben were to die, we wanted to donate any of his organs which could be used. At 4.10 a.m. on Saturday, 9 June, our fourth child, Benjamin, died. Less than 48 hours after appearing well and healthy, our precious, beautiful child was gone. All the struggles, research, appointments, treatments, hospital stays – everything concerned with Ben and the fight to prolong his life was over.

Together, Tony and I gently wrapped Ben in a blanket and wept. I remember crying his name over and over, telling him how much we loved him, how special he was, that we didn't want him to leave us. I wanted to hold him and never let him go.

Devastating and terrible though Ben's dying was, it was made more bearable by the loving way in which the staff treated him and the support we had from Acorns – one of the very few children's hospices in the country which offers support to families who have children with life-threatening conditions. Acorns is close to the hospital and our other children stayed there the night, so we could be with Ben. Now the social worker, Steve, brought them to see him for the last time. After we had washed and dressed Ben, we laid him in a cot with his sheepskin fleece – he had slept on it ever since he was a new-born baby – placing his cuddly toys around him, just as he always had them in his cot at home. Then we went out to see Lucy, Matthew and Thomas. I have a memory of their sleepy, worried faces and then their sadness and tears. They wanted to see him and it seemed the most natural thing they should do. They had always visited him in hospital and were completely involved in his life. Now they needed to be part of his death.

Ben's short life made an impact on many people, as we know from the hundreds of messages we received. It has changed me too. I used to think ahead, working myself up about tomorrow and next month and next year. Ben taught me to live for today. Despite the tragedy of Ben's death, I haven't been destroyed. I am stronger, more independent. I don't worry about ridiculous things. The people nothing ever happens to are the ones who worry. They carry on about a scratch on the car or someone forgetting their birthday. When I have a bad day and the children are yelling, I am reminded that they are here, and I am glad to hear them.

I feel now I can talk to anyone, argue

with experts and do anything for my family. I am no better or stronger than any other parent but I have something to offer, because of what I have been through. Ben will always belong to the five of us and all who cared for him. There is a sense in which we can never be separated.'

Sue Pasternak has set up a support group for families whose children have heart and lung transplants. She also raises funds for the hospice Acorns – a registered charity.

(*Good Housekeeping*, December 1990)

activity

Care and support for those who are dying and their families

1 How can someone help a person who is suffering from bereavement? Draw up a list of positive ways in which you could show your concern.
2 Find out about the hospice movement:
   - When did the hospice movement start?
   - What are the main aims of hospice care?
3 Interview anyone who has suffered a bereavement and make brief notes.
4 Find out about the work of support groups for bereavement:
   - CRUSE
   - The Compassionate Friends
   - The Stillbirth and Neonatal Death Society (SANDS)
   - The Child Bereavement Trust

Sensory impairment

This is the general name given to the group of disabilities which involve disorders of the senses: sight, hearing, touch, taste or smell.

BLINDNESS AND PARTIAL SIGHT

The picture of total darkness conjured up by the word 'blindness' is inaccurate. Only about 18 per cent of blind people in the UK are affected to this degree. The other 82 per cent have some remaining sight. In the UK there are just over one million blind and partially sighted people, of whom 40 per cent are classed as blind and 60 per cent classed as partially sighted.

Causes of visual impairment in children

The main causes of visual impairment in children are:

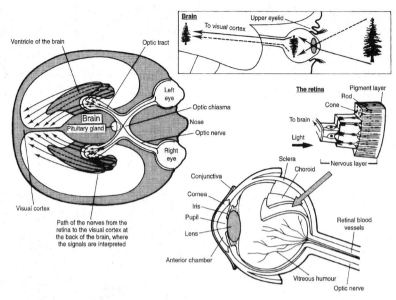

Figure 3.13 The eye and how it works

- anomalies of the eyes from birth such as cataracts – cloudiness of the lens
- nystagmus – involuntary jerkiness of the eyes
- optic atrophy – damage to the optic nerve
- retinopathy of prematurity – abnormal development of retinas in premature babies
- hereditary factors such as retinoblastoma – a tumour of the retina which is often inherited.

Glaucoma and diabetic retinopathy are quite rare in children, but are common causes of visual impairment in adults.

Causes of visual impairment in adults

Four out of five people with impaired vision are over retirement age. Among the over-75s, one person in seven is blind or partially sighted. The main causes of visual impairment in adults are:

Among people of working age (ages 16–64):

- diabetes and diabetic retinopathy – diabetic retinopathy is characterised by tiny balloon-like swellings of the capillaries in the retina, leakage of fluid from the capillaries and bleeding into the retina
- hereditary disorders of the retina
- degeneration of the macula and posterior pole – this refers to degeneration of the central area of the retina and usually occurs in old age
- optic atrophy
- glaucoma – a condition in which the pressure of the fluid in the eye is so high that it causes damage to the nerve fibres and gradual loss of vision.

In the older age group (65 years and over):

- degeneration of the macula and posterior pole
- glaucoma
- cataracts and diabetic retinopathy.

Figure 3.14 demonstrates the effects of some of these eye conditions on vision.

(a)

(b)

(c)

(d)

(e)

Figure 3.14 Impressions of what people with certain eye conditions may see (a) the whole picture (b) Cataracts make everything look misty and blurred (c) Macular degeneration – central vision may be lost while side vision remains (d) Severe glaucoma and some other eye conditions can result in tunnel vision (e) Diabetic retinopathy leads to patchy and blurred vision

Treatment

Some conditions which cause visual impairment are treatable, particularly if detected at an early stage. For example:

- glaucoma can be halted by medical or surgical means
- cataract may be treated by removal of the lens.

Laser therapy is now being used to correct various visual defects.

Education and training

More than 55 per cent of the visually impaired children in school attend mainstream schools along with sighted children, where most will have a *statement of special educational needs* which details the support and special equipment they need. This is provided by the school, with advice and support from the Local Education Authority Visual Impairment Service and other sources of information, advice and training, such as the Royal National Institute for the Blind (RNIB). Many move on to further education colleges and universities, using special grants to enable them to pay for readers and to buy special tape recorders to help them in their studies.

Specialist counselling and vocational training are available for those of working age, and may be accessed through local authorities, the RNIB and colleges of further education.

activity

The RNIB has produced an excellent booklet, *One step at a time*, for parents of visually impaired children. It gives practical advice and tips on such topics as developing the senses, establishing routines and learning to walk. The RNIB and the British Toy and Hobby Association have jointly produced a free booklet on popular toys and games for blind and partially sighted children. Tutors and/or students may wish to send away for copies of the two booklets (see 'Useful addresses' section, page 213).

1 Working in small groups, plan and mount a display on children with visual

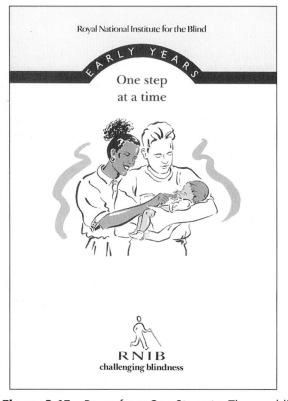
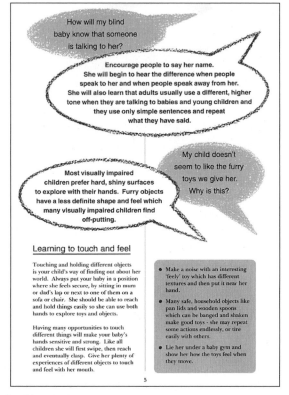

Figure 3.15 Pages from *One Step at a Time*, published by the RNIB

impairment. Using the booklets as a guide, each small group should plan and mount a display on all of the following topics:

- developing the senses
- establishing routines
- movement games
- play and toys.

When the displays are up, each group should evaluate each other's display, using a set of criteria agreed beforehand. For example, is the information presented in an easy-to-understand format? Does the material used illustrate the points effectively?

2 Try to contact a local group of parents of visually impaired children and invite them to view the display; health visitors and/or social services departments may be able to make the first contact.

Visual impairment and adolescence

It is often at adolescence that the full impact of visual impairment is felt, and young people have to face the fact that they are visually impaired for life. Sometimes this emotional trauma results in a period of mourning over the lost or absent vision. The main problems associated with visual impairment are:

- **Restricted mobility**: at a time when many of their sighted friends are able to drive a car, this can be a major cause of stress.
- **Restricted social opportunities**: unless they have had a full programme of mobility training, they will be dependent upon fully-sighted people to take them out.
- **Reliance on others for choice of dress-style**: those with severe visual impairment may never have been able to choose their own clothes and may have been guided by adult tastes, rather than by their peers.
- **The skills of eating appropriately**: eating in a group situation is fraught with difficulty if you can't see clearly and many young people may always ask for the same meal, which they know is relatively easy to manage.

It is important for the development of self-esteem that young people with a visual impairment receive personal counselling to help them to come to terms with their particular impairment, and specialist training in the important areas of self-presentation skills, communication, the manner of dressing and the skills of eating appropriately.

Meeting blind people

The RNIB produces leaflets which give advice on meeting blind people and on how to *guide* a blind person. Many sighted people feel awkward and ill at ease when first meeting blind people because they feel they don't know how to behave. Some guidelines are:

- Talk naturally. Never address all your remarks to a companion as if the blind person does not exist.
- When you greet a blind or partially sighted person, say who you are in case he or she does not recognise you or your voice. Introduce anyone else who is present; try to indicate where they are placed in the room.
- When offering a handshake, say something like, 'Shall we shake hands?'

- Do not leave someone talking to an empty space; before moving away, say that you are about to leave.
- Many blind people appreciate help to cross a road or find a shop, but don't feel offended if your offer of help is rejected.

- First, ask if you can help and, if so, how the person would like to be guided.
- Always lead a blind person from the front, never push him or her ahead of you.
- Explain things he or she can't see, such as a kerb or a slope in the ground.

activity

An exercise in empathy

The following exercise cannot give a real experience of blindness, but may help to promote understanding. It should be carried out in pairs.

1 One person ties a blindfold (e.g. a scarf) around the eyes and the other person escorts him or her around the college or neighbourhood. On return, the sighted one offers the 'blind' person a drink and a sandwich.
2 Then swap roles and repeat the exercise.

Discuss and evaluate the activity. How did it feel to be so dependent on someone else? How did it feel to be responsible for someone else?
3 Draw up a list of practical points to help others when offering refreshment and guidance to someone who is blind.
4 Find out about the aids available for those with visual impairment, including the Braille alphabet and Moon, which is a less well-known method of reading by touch.

DEAFNESS AND PARTIAL HEARING

Deafness is often called the 'hidden' disability. As with blindness, total deafness is rare and is usually congenital (present from birth). Partial deafness is generally the result of an ear disease, injury or degeneration associated with the ageing process. There are two types of deafness:

- **conductive** – when there is faulty transmission of sound from the outer ear to the inner ear
- **sensorineural** – when sounds that do reach the inner ear fail to be transmitted to the brain.

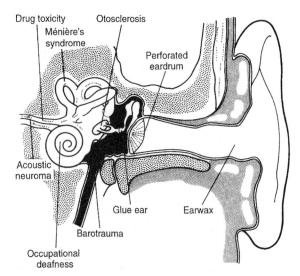

Figure 3.16 Some possible causes of deafness, showing the part of the ear affected

Causes of conductive deafness

- **Earwax**: some people experience a build-up of cerumen, a waxy discharge, which can form a plug in the eardrum. This is the most common cause of deafness in adults.
- **Otosclerosis**: the stapes loses its normal mobility (see Figure 3.16).
- **Otitis media**: infection of the middle ear, common in children.
- **Glue ear**: a build-up of sticky fluid in the middle ear. This condition mostly affects children under eight years old.

Causes of sensorineural deafness

- **Heredity**: there may be an inherited fault in a chromosome.
- **Birth injury**: when the birth is prolonged or complicated, e.g. by the use of forceps.
- **Rubella**: there may be damage to the developing foetus if the mother is infected with the rubella (German measles) virus during pregnancy (see page 57).
- **Jaundice**: if a new-born baby has severe jaundice, there may be damage to the inner ear.
- **Damage to the cochlea and/or labyrinth**: this may result from injury, viral infection or prolonged exposure to loud noise.
- **Menière's disease**: a rare disorder in which deafness, vertigo and **tinnitus** result from the accumulation of fluid within the labyrinth in the inner ear.

Diagnosis

Hearing tests are performed as part of a routine assessment of child development. Early detection of any hearing defect is vital in order that the best possible help is offered at the time when development is at its fastest.

Treatment

For conductive hearing loss:

- syringing of the ear in the case of earwax; this procedure should be carried out by a doctor or nurse as amateur attempts can damage the eardrum
- surgical correction of defect
- hearing aid.

For sensorineural hearing loss:
- a hearing aid – about one quarter of the population over 70 years old need a hearing aid
- special training – language acquisition, auditory training, speech therapy, and perceptual motor training.

A bilingual approach using British Sign Language (BSL) and verbal speech is now often recommended. (See Chapter 5 for further information on hearing aids and training methods.)

Problems associated with hearing impairment

- **Communication**: isolation may result from the deaf child's inability to hear the familiar voices and household noises that the hearing child takes for granted. It is important to encourage all forms of communication from as early as possible, not just the acquisition of speech.
- **Lack of auditory stimulation**: this may lead to delayed development.
- **Potential for injury**: related to failure to detect warning sounds, e.g. traffic or warning shouts.
- **Anxiety and coping difficulties**: related to reduced social interaction and loneliness.
- **Parental anxiety**: related to having a child with impaired hearing.

Guidelines for carers

Babies and children with impaired hearing

- A baby with hearing impairment may not show the 'startle' reaction to a loud noise; this is evident shortly after birth.
- A baby of about four months will visibly relax and smile at the sound of her mother's voice, even before she can see her; if the baby does not show this response, there *may* be some hearing loss.
- If babbling starts and then stops after a few weeks, this is often an indication of hearing loss.
- Children with hearing loss will be much more observant and visually aware than hearing children; for example, they may respond to doorbells and telephones by 'reading' the body language of those around them and responding appropriately.
- Toys that make a lot of noise are popular, because children can feel the vibration, even if they cannot hear the sound; dancing to music is also popular for the same reason.
- A child with a profound hearing loss may react quite normally and even turn round in response to someone's approach; she may be using her other senses to compensate for loss of hearing – for example she may notice a smell of perfume, or see the reflection of the person in a window or other glass surface.

Early diagnosis and treatment can make a significant difference to the language development and learning potential of a child with hearing impairment.

Adults with hearing impairment

When meeting people who are deaf

- Do not make assumptions about a person's ability to communicate, or the ways in which they do it; always ask the person to tell you.
- Remember that deaf people who use sign language find this the easiest method of communication.
- Do not shout when talking to a deaf or hearing-impaired person; shouting will only distort the sounds received.
- Make sure background noise, for example noise from radios, televisions or conversations, is reduced.
- Check that a hearing aid, if worn, is in good working order.
- Do not assume that everyone who is deaf can lip-read. Always ask the person when you first meet them.
- If they do lip-read, remember that this skill is never completely reliable. It requires intense concentration and is very tiring.

When meeting a person who is lip-reading

- Look directly at them and speak slowly and clearly; obtain eye contact.
- Speak with facial expressions, gestures and body movements which emphasise the words you use. Note: Only three out of ten words are visible on the lips.
- Face the light and keep hands, cigarettes and food away from your face while speaking.
- If necessary, attract the person's attention with a light touch on their shoulder or a wave of your hand.

activity

1 Preparing a care plan

A six-year-old child, Tom, is admitted to hospital for a tonsillectomy (surgical removal of the tonsils). He has a severe hearing impairment of the sensorineural type. Draw up a list of questions that you should ask Tom's parents to enable a specific care plan to be formulated.

- Work out how to ensure continuity of care from home to hospital in order to minimise frustration and fear for Tom.
- Use the activities of daily living model (see page 12) to ensure that you are meeting all Tom's needs.

2 Research into hearing impairment

Arrange to visit the local child health clinic or invite a health visitor to your college. Find out the following information:

- How and when are hearing tests carried out?
- If the child 'fails' a test, how is a follow-up test carried out and by whom?
- What is involved in the operation for glue ear (myringotomy and insertion of grommets)? How many such operations are carried out in your district health authority each year?

IMPAIRMENTS OF THE OTHER SENSES

The sense of smell is known as the *olfactory* sense and is closely related to the sense of taste, known as the *gustatory* sense. The sense of taste is rarely affected on its own, although this can occur as a result of head injury or a disease causing degeneration of the nerves.

The sense of touch – *tactile* sensation – is most marked in the palm and fingertips. Loss of tactile sensation can occur in association with paralysis, or conditions such as leprosy or alcoholism. A severe burn may cause damage to the touch receptors in skin tissues, resulting in lack of tactile sensation.

RESOURCES

Under the Eye of the Clock by Christopher
  Nolan
  Published by Weidenfeld & Nicholson
  (1987)

A wonderful book (winner of the 1987
Whitbread Biography Award) written by a
man who has cerebral palsy. Christopher
Nolan nearly died at birth from asphyxiation,
but survived with severe brain damage, cut off
in his own silent world, restricted by a mute
and paralysed body. He tells how he managed
to break the barriers of that impossible
cocooned existence so that the reader can see
into the thoughts and realities of a state
nobody has ever known about.

Christopher – A Silent Life by Margaret Brock
  Published by Bedford Square Press of the
  National Council for Voluntary
  Organisations (1984)

Margaret Brock had rubella (German measles)
in the first weeks of pregnancy. Her son
Christopher was born totally blind and
profoundly deaf. In the book, Margaret Brock
writes about the day-to-day experiences of life
in a family 'containing' a deaf–blind, non-
communicating child from birth until
adulthood.

My Left Foot by Christy Brown
  Published by Martin, Secker & Warburg
  (1954)
  Also a feature film (1979)

My Left Foot tells the story of Christy Brown
who had cerebral palsy and learned to paint
and write with one foot.

CHAPTER 4

SPECIAL NEEDS – LEARNING DIFFICULTIES, BEHAVIOURAL DISORDERS AND MENTAL HEALTH PROBLEMS

The nature and possible causes of learning difficulties or disabilities are described – hereditary and congenital factors, developmental factors, birth injuries, accidents, disease-related and neurological factors. The chapter explores the needs of people with severe learning difficulties and moderate learning difficulties, and, as with physical disabilities, the main focus is on the effects such difficulties have on daily life. Behavioural disorders, such as Attention Deficit Hyperactivity Disorder (ADHD), and mental health problems, such as Alzheimer's disease, eating disorders and depression are also described in terms of the special needs involved. Homelessness and substance abuse are included here as they also engender special needs and pose problems for health and social care provision.

Learning difficulties

The terms 'mental handicap' and 'mental retardation' are now thought by many to do too much damage, and the less harsh 'learning disability' and 'learning difficulty' are used instead. (In the USA, the term 'mental retardation' is usually employed.) When someone is described as having a general developmental delay or a general learning difficulty, it means two things:

● that their intelligence is towards the lower end of the intelligence scale on which we all fit somewhere

● that their social skills (their ability to adapt to new situations and interact with others) are not as good as those of other people.

Some people are born with a learning difficulty, for example those with Down's syndrome. Others become disabled through a disease, such as meningitis, or through accident, such as an injury to the brain. It is important not to confuse mental illness and learning difficulty. A learning difficulty is usually something that people are born with and live with, and often learn to cope with; a mental illness can afflict anybody, and if someone does become mentally ill, they can often be made better. Having problems with learning and the development of social skills does not mean that people with learning difficulties can't learn, develop and adapt; it simply means that they take longer and may not go so far.

DOWN'S SYNDROME

Down's syndrome is the largest cause of learning difficulty. It affects about 1 in 650 babies born in the UK. The condition was first described by Dr John Langdon Down in 1866, but it was not until 1959 that the cause – the presence of an extra chromosome – was discovered. As the extra chromosome is number 21 (three instead of two number 21 chromosomes), the syndrome is also called Trisomy 21.

Characteristics of people with Down's syndrome

Down's syndrome is normally suspected soon after birth because of certain distinguishing characteristics; chromosome tests are then carried out to confirm the diagnosis. These characteristics include:

● eyes that slant slightly upwards and outwards; there is also often an *epicanthic fold* – a fold of skin that runs vertically between the two eyelids at the inner corner of the eye
● a face that appears rather flattened
● a relatively large, sometimes protruding, tongue in a relatively small mouth
● hands that are broad, with short fingers and a little finger that curves inwards; the palm may have only one crease running across it
● a deep groove between the first and second toe that extends as a long crease on the side of the foot
● hypotonia – reduced muscle tone which results in floppiness; this improves without treatment as the child gets older
● a below average weight and length at birth.

Between 40 and 50 per cent of people with Down's syndrome also have a heart defect.

Children with Down's syndrome develop and learn in the same way as children without the condition, but at a slower rate. Table 4.1 compares the major developmental 'milestones' attained by children with Down's syndrome with those attained by ordinary children.

Care needs of people with Down's syndrome

These will obviously vary from person to person, and the needs will also be different according to family circumstances and any associated physical health problems. Most of these care needs are the same as for any developing child; it is usually only the time scale that is different. Some needs are:

● help with bodily functions
● supervision to ensure safety – some

	Down's syndrome		Ordinary	
	Average age	**Age range**	**Average age**	**Age range**
Gross motor				
Sits alone	11 months	6–30 months	6 months	5–9 months
Crawls	15 months	8–22 months	9 months	6–12 months
Stands	20 months	$1–3\frac{1}{4}$ years	11 months	8–17 months
Walks alone	26 months	1–4 years	14 months	9–18 months
Language				
First word	23 months	1–4 years	12 months	8–23 months
Two-word phrases	3 years	$2–7\frac{1}{2}$ years	2 years	15–32 months
Personal/social				
Responsive smile	3 months	$1\frac{1}{2}$–5 months	$1\frac{1}{2}$ months	1–3 months
Finger-feeds	18 months	10–24 months	10 months	7–14 months
Drinks from cup (unassisted)	23 months	12–32 months	13 months	9–17 months
Uses spoon	29 months	13–39 months	14 months	12–20 months
Bowel control	$3\frac{3}{4}$ years	2–7 years	22 months	16–42 months
Dresses self (not fastenings)	$7\frac{1}{4}$ years	$3\frac{1}{2}–8\frac{1}{4}$ years	4 years	$3\frac{1}{4}$–5 years

Table 4.1   Major developmental milestones

Source: M. Selikowitz (1990) *Down's Syndrome, the facts*, Oxford University Press. By permission of Oxford University Press

children take a relatively long time before they can recognise and avoid common dangers, so they will need closer supervision both inside and outside the home

- stimulation to maximise potential achievement.

Adults with Down's syndrome may continue to require help in fulfilling their needs; how independent they can be will be determined by the severity of learning difficulty. For example, a group of three or four people with learning difficulties may be placed in a house together where they cope with daily living activities without continual supervision. Perhaps a social worker visits once or twice a week to check on their welfare. While they may not be capable of completely independent living, they may not need supervision to ensure their own safety nor frequent attention in relation to their bodily functions.

The following case study is a true 'snapshot' biography, written by her parents, of a young girl who has Down's syndrome.

CASE STUDY

Hannah

When Hannah was born we suspected straight away that she had Down's syndrome. Our thoughts were confirmed by the **consultant** the following morning. Many children with Down's syndrome find it hard to suck, and with Hannah breast-feeding proved very difficult; but with the support of a wonderful nursery nurse at the hospital, we managed it. During this time, a midwife noticed that Hannah appeared to be blue around the face, which suggested that she had a possible heart condition.

At less than a week old, we took Hannah to a London hospital to have a heart scan. She was diagnosed as having an atrio-ventricular septal defect (AVSD). Corrective surgery would involve patching up two holes and reconstructing a heart valve. We were informed by a consultant that if surgery were not performed, then Hannah would probably not live beyond her teens. The consultant suggested that we choose not to follow the surgery option, since the quality of life for a teenager with Down's syndrome was poor. At one week old, Hannah was being discriminated against, because she was born with Down's syndrome!

At home we were visited by a Portage worker, a home-based early educational intervention service. Hannah was set different tasks each week for which achievable targets were set. Hannah's babbling and motor skills were developing as one would expect for a child with Down's syndrome. She still had difficulty sucking and

eating baby foods. When she was a year old we were visited by a speech therapist and physiotherapist. More tasks were given and Makaton signs were introduced to aid her communication and eating skills.

Regular visits continued to be made to various hospitals. We decided that Hannah would undergo corrective heart surgery. She was on medication for her heart condition, and her hearing and eyesight were being monitored.

Hannah had her open heart surgery at 14 months old at a different London children's hospital. The corrective surgery was successful, but she caught two infections during the recovery phase while still in hospital. As a result she became totally floppy again and lost her spontaneous babbling. After five weeks in hospital, Hannah was well enough to return home even though her muscle tone was very poor.

Visits to various hospitals continued, and Hannah was gradually weaned off her medicines. With this major hurdle over, we could begin to concentrate on other areas of her development. For the first time Hannah began to eat real food. Chocolate buttons were an early favourite! We had heard how many children with Down's syndrome tended to be obese, but Hannah was tiny and needed feeding up! We also knew that children with Down's syndrome were 'loving'. Well, Hannah was very affectionate towards some people, but understandably feared any medical staff. Hannah's verbal and motor skills developed at an extremely slow rate. Her peers who also had Down's syndrome were beginning to walk and talk, but Hannah was not. It was apparent that her level of understanding was developing much more quickly than her expressive skills.

We were very keen that Hannah should go to an integrated nursery. We eventually found a lovely nursery, but would need to find a volunteer to be with Hannah throughout the sessions she attended. Hannah stayed at nursery for several years. Her volunteers changed, although on several occasions I had to go in to support her myself. It was not until her final year that the Local Education Authority began to fund nursery support for children with Down's syndrome. She then received regular professional support, and for the first time I didn't have to worry if her helper would not turn up.

Hannah was still not walking or talking. She used Makaton to sign her needs, and to read simple books. She was able to count up to five, by pointing to the numbers. She had been allowed to spend an extra year at the nursery, but by the time she was six the local authority was keen to place her in a special school or a special unit. We opposed and fought against this. For the following year, Hannah was educated at home. She developed further many of her basic skills. Finally, after numerous meetings, the authority finally agreed to allow her to go to our local school.

Hannah has settled into school life quickly and easily and has amazed everyone despite all of her difficulties. Although she can be stubborn, Hannah is also very cooperative. She loves the social aspects of

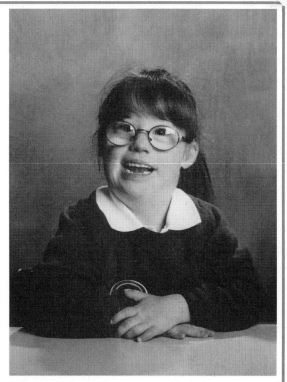

Figure 4.1 Hannah

school life, as well as the learning activities. The school, children and other parents hold a wonderfully supportive attitude towards her as an individual. Hannah receives the full-time support that she is entitled to and, as long as she is progressing and happy at school, we will continue to fight for an integrated education for her.

It could not be said that Hannah is typical of a child who has Down's syndrome. (In fact, there is no such thing as a typical child who has Down's syndrome.) Hannah's physical and verbal difficulties make everyday life harder for her, but her strong personality, charm and determination are helping her get on with life and have earned her the respect of her parents, teachers, helper and fellow classmates.

— activity —

to integration

Find out about the education and support offered to children with Down's syndrome in your area.

1 What is available for children with Down's syndrome of nursery school age, of primary school age and of secondary school age?

2 What are the advantages of inclusive education for children with Down's syndrome, and for their peers?

3 Find out about Makaton as a method of communication.

FRAGILE X SYNDROME

Fragile X syndrome is the most common *inherited* form of learning difficulty. It gets its name from a gene on the X chromosome. The range of effects on the individual is very wide. Table 4.2 lists some of the main characteristics which may be associated with Fragile X syndrome; however, it is rare for *all* the features listed to be present.

AUTISM

Autism (or autistic spectrum disorder) is a rare developmental disorder which impairs the child's understanding of his or her environment. The estimated prevalence rate of autistic spectrum disorders, including Asperger syndrome, is 56 per 10,000 people in the UK.

Causes of autism

There is no known cause of autism but, because about one-quarter of children with autism have neurological symptoms, many specialists now believe there may be a physical and/or genetic factor. Two theories are that autism may be related to abnormal levels of essential fatty acids in the blood or to an abnormal blood flow through the brain. Autism occurs in all parts of the world; boys are affected more often than girls, in the ratio of 4 : 1.

Features of autism

A child with autism may:

- lack awareness of other people
- avoid eye-to-eye contact
- prefer to play alone
- be oversensitive to certain sounds
- be extremely resistant to change and become obsessed with one particular topic or idea
- have difficulty in understanding and using normal speech patterns; echolalia – an automatic repetition of what is said to the child – is common
- show abnormal body movements, e.g. arm flapping, flicking fingers for hours on end, grimacing, rocking and charging in different directions at great speed
- have sudden screaming fits
- show an isolated special skill, e.g. drawing, music or an outstanding rote memory.

Diagnosis

A diagnosis of autism is not usually made until the child is two years old, although

Behaviour

Over-activity	Unable to settle for long to any one activity; always rushing around
Demanding attention	Demands for attention are persistent and insistent
Hand-flapping	Usually at times of anxiety or distress
Excitability	Acting without thinking first, responding impulsively to first perceptions

Speech and language

Dysarthria	Difficulty in articulating sounds
Dysphasia	Difficulty in selecting the words with which to speak
Echolalia	Compulsive repetition of the last word or phrase spoken to them
Palilalia	Compulsive repetition of their own words or phrases
Lack of fluency	Speech is often rapid and digresses from subject

Emotional and social development

Emotional lability	Tendency to react emotionally to relatively minor upsets
Sensitivity	Extra sensitive to any perceived criticism
Security	Need for constant reassurance; often appears to need a routine
Reaction to environment	Displays variability in reactions to 'busy' environments; appears overwhelmed if a lot is going on around them, particularly in noisy settings

Cognitive development

Verbal skills	Verbal skills are better than reasoning skills
Abstract reasoning	Tendency to be diverted by attention to irrelevant aspects of tasks and events
Understanding of maths	Difficulty with number concepts and basic arithmetical processes
Vocabulary	Relative strengths in vocabulary and associated verbal areas

Table 4.2   Some characteristics associated with fragile X syndrome

parents may have noticed a lack of curiosity in their child, with poor sleeping and feeding patterns and general unresponsiveness in the first year.

Support and education for people with autism

There is no known effective treatment apart from medication to control the asso-

Figure 4.2   Some characteristics of a person with autism

ciated problems of epilepsy and hyperactivity. Many therapies are being tried, including:

- **Holding therapy**: parents group together for long periods of time and try to foster emotional responsiveness by firm holding techniques.
- **Behaviour therapy**: acceptable behaviours are rewarded; unacceptable behaviours are discouraged.

- **Daily life therapy**: developed by Dr Kitahara in the Boston Higashi school in the USA, this form of therapy offers a programme of physical education and age-appropriate lessons in a residential setting.
- **Lovaas method**: developed by Professor Ivaar Lovaas in California, USA, this method offers an intensive programme of therapy using behaviour modification techniques.

A person with severe autism will need constant one-to-one care, requiring considerable patience and skill on the part of all family members. Any changes to the person's routine must be carefully planned.

Early childhood education, for example at a nursery or playgroup, will help the family integrate into the community. Most children with autism attend local schools for children with severe learning difficulties; others require residential care – the National Autistic Society runs several schools which offer day, weekly or termly facilities.

Some people with autism remain mute and withdrawn all their lives. At present, there are few colleges or centres which have the necessary resources and skilled staff to cater for people with autism. Most adults with autism continue to need care and supervision, but some find work in open or sheltered employment.

ASPERGER SYNDROME

Most people with Asperger syndrome represent the less severe end of the autistic spectrum. Language delay is not as common, but there are often problems with communication and the child with Asperger syndrome is usually aware of his or her disability. Characteristics of people with this syndrome are:

- social naivety
- good grammatical language, but language used only for own interests
- very specialised interests, often highly academic, e.g. movement of the planets or railway timetables
- lack of common sense arising from unawareness of their environment.

activity

1 Find out if there is any special provision for children with autism in your local area.
2 Find out about the work of the National Autistic Society.
3 List the social skills required to participate fully in daily activities in a reception class. Try to describe the difficulties a child with autism may have in integrating.
4 What help and support is available to the family of a child with autism?
5 What might the effects be on siblings of living with a child with autism?

If possible, arrange to watch the film *Rain Man* (see 'Resources' section at the end of this chapter).

THE NEEDS OF PEOPLE WITH COMMUNICATION DIFFICULTIES

Children experiencing difficulties with some aspect of communication form the largest group of children with special needs in the pre-school years (Law, 1992). Language involves:

- listening or watching and understanding (*reception* of language)
- communicating, which involves facial expressions, gestures, speech or signing (*expression* of language).

A person who has a hearing impairment or an autistic spectrum disorder may have difficulties in both the reception and the expression of language; this will result in a greater need for specialist resources, and – for children – a statement of educational needs will have to be made. Difficulties with communication that are mainly expressive tend to show as a speech or language delay and usually require less resources and may not be subject to a statement. It is estimated that 50 per cent of children with language difficulties, particularly those of the receptive kind, also have emotional and behavioural difficulties. There is also a strong link between language difficulty and **attention deficit hyperactivity disorder (ADHD)**.

Meeting people with speech difficulties

Any speech difficulty may cause embarrassment and frustration on both sides.

- Give your whole attention to the person. Be encouraging and patient.
- Do not correct or speak for the person. Wait quietly while the person talks and resist the temptation to finish sentences.
- Where possible, ask questions that require short answers or a nod or shake of the head.
- Do not pretend to understand when you have not understood. Repeat what you do not understand and the person's reaction will guide you.

DYSLEXIA

Dyslexia is a specific learning difficulty characterised by difficulty in coping with written symbols. Some problems encountered by the person with dyslexia are:

- language problems
- sequencing difficulties
- visual perception problems
- poor short-term memory
- a lack of spatial awareness
- short concentration span
- directional confusion
- reversal of letters and numbers
- stress and fear of failure.

Every child with dyslexia has a different pattern of difficulties. Intelligence is usually unaffected, but the problem may seem more obvious in intelligent children. Dyslexia is a very vague term which tends to be used to cover all kinds of difficulties, ranging from mild problems with spelling to complete illiteracy (inability to read or write). Recent research has shown that the brains of people with dyslexia are 'wired' differently from other people's. Micro-anatomy carried out on their brains after death shows that while there is a lack of efficiency in the left brain hemisphere which relates to language ability, there is *increased* efficiency in the side of the brain which dictates spatial ability. Visual spatial skills seem superior in people with dyslexia; their ability to see the world in a more vivid, three-dimensional way points to a link between artistic talent and dyslexia.

Dyslexia is often seen as a middle-class

excuse for academic non-achievement. Early identification of the problem can greatly reduce the difficulties, both for the individual with dyslexia and for their school and family. Teaching strategies include:

- regular praise and rewards – many children with dyslexia have poor self-esteem and see themselves as failures within the school system
- keeping records of each lesson plan, so that each lesson builds upon the success of the previous one
- 'scaffolding' work – structuring the work into a series of small steps which supports the learning
- the use of specific teaching aids, e.g. special phonic 'flash' cards for letter recognition
- the use of concrete and visual ways of explaining, e.g. presenting instructions in the form of diagrams, or essay plans laid out as patterns.

A student taking a degree course in sculpture and fashion design at art college was never diagnosed as having a dyslexia-based problem at school. She describes her experience as follows:

> I passed my A levels in art and design and the history of art before I passed my GCSE English. It took me six attempts before I managed to gain GCSE English. When I look at a page of writing, it's the white space around the black word which stands out most clearly, not the other way round. Also I have a problem with remembering words – when I'm reading a page, by the time I've reached the bottom I've usually forgotten what the first paragraph says. I see things in three dimensions and find the best way to express myself is through sculpture.

ATTENTION DEFICIT HYPERACTIVITY DISORDER

Attention deficit hyperactivity disorder (ADHD) fits into the category of specific learning difficulty. Children may show some or all of the following characteristics:

- difficulty remaining seated when asked to do so
- difficulty playing quietly
- difficulty in sharing and taking turns in group situations
- often losing things necessary for tasks or activities at school or at home, e.g. books, pencils, etc.
- often talking excessively
- difficulty sustaining attention in tasks or play activities
- being easily distracted by extraneous stimuli
- interrupting others, e.g. butting into other children's games
- often appearing not to listen when being spoken to
- often engaging in physically dangerous activities without considering the possible consequences, e.g. running across the road without looking
- appearing restless; often fidgeting with hands or feet.
- an inability to focus attention on relevant detail at an age when such control is expected.

ADHD is sometimes initially diagnosed as an autistic spectrum disorder as many of the features are common to both disorders. It is estimated that about half of children with ADHD also show behavioural (or conduct) disorders.

The cause of ADHD is not known, but there is growing evidence to show that a pattern of hyperactivity is inherited and also that there may be a biological cause, perhaps due to a slower **metabolism** of glucose by the brain. Treatment is by a stimulant medication (usually Ritalin) which often has an immediate improving effect on the child's behaviour; arriving at the correct dosage for the individual, however, takes time and a high degree of cooperation between school and parents. Daily feedback from the child's class teacher is essential for the treatment to be effective in the long term.

Emotional and behavioural difficulties

Any behaviour that causes a problem to others falls within this category. Such difficulties include:

- **conduct disorders** – bullying, aggression, disobedience and delinquency
- **anxiety and withdrawal** – depression and eating disorders
- **socialised aggression** – children who have experienced rejection by their peers and others show a marked tendency to band together, thus supporting and reinforcing their anti-social behaviour.

Assessment of need in this area is difficult and before a child is included in this category, an educational psychologist will look at both the *intensity* and the *frequency* of the child's behaviour. Behaviour that is highly inappropriate in one social context may be quite acceptable in another situation.

CONDUCT DISORDERS

Young children may show early signs of conduct disorders by throwing regular temper tantrums. There is a strong argument for considering the origins of conduct disorders to be *environmental*. Some contributory factors are:

- failure in early parental discipline – the form of discipline may be too lax or too severe, non-existent or inconsistent
- failure to develop important attachment bonds
- poor peer acceptance, or even rejection by peers
- direct reinforcement for aggressive behaviour within the family – in other words, violence begets violence
- economic and social deprivation, e.g. feelings of frustration from poor living conditions and no prospect of improvement
- genetic input – there is some evidence to suggest that there is a genetic factor in conduct disorders; a study by Mednick and Hutchings (1978) found that adopted sons were more likely to become criminals if their biological parents were criminals, even when their adoptive parents were law-abiding.

Not all problem behaviours centre around aggression. Children may lie, steal, bully and swear. Bullying, in particular, has received a great deal of attention in the media and in schools. Psychologists now emphasise three aspects of bullying:

1 **the physical aspect** – fighting, punching, pushing and kicking
2 **mental subordination** – 'put-downs', taunting and name-calling
3 **social exclusion** – ignoring and deliber-

ately avoiding and excluding someone from one's company.

Labelling a child as a 'bully' is a negative response to the problem.

THE PRINCIPLES AND TECHNIQUES OF BEHAVIOUR MANAGEMENT

Certain general principles underpin good practice when working with children.

- 'Contain' a child's anger in a safe way so that the child does not feel out of control. This needs to be practised by someone who has a good relationship with the child. It may take the form of quietly holding the child, or simply 'being there' for them.
- Discuss sensitive issues with older children.
- Give children the language they need to express themselves; this includes eye contact, body language and gestures.
- Praise and reward positive behaviour. A child who is disrupting the group will be seeking attention; children are best helped if they realise that they will have warm positive attention when they are cooperative.
- Teach children to be assertive, rather than being aggressive or timid.
- Remember the needs of all children: personal space, friends, one-to-one attention, to feel secure, and to feel part of the group.
- Distract young children; do not confront them.
- Provide activities and equipment through which children can play out their strong emotions.
- Being a good role model.

Various techniques are used to deal with problem or unwanted behaviour, including:

- ABC analysis of behaviour
- behaviour modification
- play therapy
- play tutoring
- Circle Time.

ABC analysis of behaviour

All behaviours, whether problematic or not, follow the same pattern, known as the ABC of behaviours:

A for Antecedents	Observable events that occur immediately before the problem behaviour occurs.
B for Behaviour	The resulting behaviour, either acceptable or unacceptable.
C for Consequences	The observable things that happen to the child immediately after the problem behaviour occurs.

Problem behaviours (B) are examined for regularly occurring antecedents (A) and consequences (C). Careful observation is necessary; by anticipating the antecedents to behaviour, adults can encourage children to change their behaviour and thus minimise conflict. It is not useful in this context to consider causes or antecedents to the problem behaviour that happened a long time ago; this is partly because we would be unable to change them in order to alter the behavioural consequence.

Example
(A) Martha (aged three) demands a chocolate biscuit; her parents deny it.

(B) Behaviour: Martha starts screaming and kicking her parents.

(C) Consequence: Parents give her the chocolate biscuit.

In this example, it would be easier to alter the *consequence* of the behaviour, using reinforcers and/or punishers.

Behaviour modification

Skinner and other behaviourists thought that adults *shape* children's behaviour and that they rehearse adult life through role play. Such shaping is achieved through the use of positive and negative reinforcements and is used to ensure that children conform to the social expectations and customs of the culture in which they grow up. The use of reinforcements needs to be consistent and effective in inducing the desired behaviour.

Some examples of positive reinforcement (rewards):

- A group of children in a reception class were given 'smiley face' stickers for work that has been very carefully completed. Most of the children tried very hard to earn these stickers but soon became discouraged if they never received a reward for their efforts. Teachers are very aware of the need to reward *effort* rather than mere performance.
- Every day that seven year old Matthew practised the piano for 30 minutes, his mother gave him 30 pence. Matthew liked seeing the money build up and each week would buy sweets and comics; the novelty, however, soon wore off and Matthew's mother then resorted to pleading and nagging to induce the desired behaviour.

An example of negative reinforcements (punishments):

- Tommy was a very active and energetic four year old who continually left his place during story-time; his behaviour distracted all the other children. At first the nursery teacher gently asked him to sit down and this method worked for a while. When Tommy began to leave his place again, the teacher spoke very harshly to him in a scolding way. Tommy's behaviour became much worse; in this case, the 'punishment' turned out to be an effective reward as Tommy received the attention he wanted.

Play therapy

Play therapists may be qualified nursery nurses, psychotherapists or qualified as a hospital play specialist. Their role is to use therapeutic play with one child or a group of children to enable them to feel more secure emotionally in potentially threatening situations. Play therapy involves:

- provision of activities and toys which satisfy the needs of children with fears and anxieties
- enabling children to gain some measure of control over their lives and what is happening around them
- establishing a good relationship with the children
- providing activities that will promote normal development.

Toys and activities can often be categorised as either *therapeutic* or *diversional*. Therapeutic toys let children 'play out' their anxieties and include clay, sand, hammer toys, medical kits, puppets and anatomically correct dolls. Diversional toys divert children's attention away from their illness or problems by promoting creativity and the enjoyment of developing new skills, they include board games, video games, paint, puppets, mobiles and rattles.

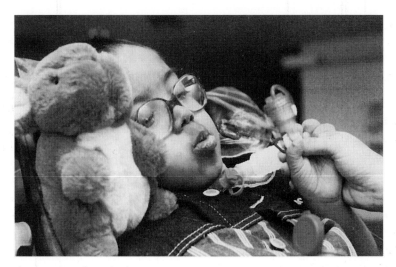

Figure 4.3 Play therapy in a hospital

Play tutoring

Play tutoring is where adults become involved with children's play. It can take many forms: extending children's ideas in imaginative play; providing praise and reward; offering a disturbed child a good deal of personal attention.

Circle Time

The use of group therapy in the form of Circle Time was developed by Jenny Mosley, an experienced special needs teacher. The key principles which underpin Circle Time are:

- the importance of listening to children
- that staff work *together* in addressing children's problems; staff left to cope with disruptive behaviour on their own can end up feeling demoralised and may resort to authoritarian methods to contain a problem without tackling its roots
- the use of interlocking incentives – e.g. half-termly certificates for good behaviour – and 'golden time' – a half hour at the end of the week when children can choose activities
- rewards for keeping clearly stated rules
- loss of rewards for breaking these rules
- that children participate in Circle Time once a week, and that teachers use the same method twice a term as a forum for discussing the development of systems to promote good behaviour, e.g. rules, incentives, rewards, sanctions, lunchtime policies, etc.

CASE STUDY

Circle Time

'I need help because I've got a very short temper and I can be very spiteful.' All eyes in the circle of children focus on a 10-year-old boy called Justin who has just made this hesitant admission. The only adult in the circle – a woman the children haven't met before – breaks the ensuing silence by wondering aloud who is going to help Justin. 'He's one of your class,' she tells the 20 other Year 6 children; 'I want you to think how you can help him.' Some of them do have suggestions for Justin, 'which is wonderful', says the adult, Jenny Mosley. 'But anybody wanting to make a proposal must use the formula: "Justin, would it help if . . . " and he, in turn, must reply courteously and with thanks.'

'Justin, would it help if you counted to 10?' asks one girl.

'I've tried that, thank you,' he replies.

'Justin, would it help if I stopped annoying you?' asks a boy.

'Yes, thank you.'

'. . . if we all told children from the older class to stop calling you names?'

'The problem is my temper makes me want to lash out. Thank you.'

According to Jenny Mosley, children are honest and do not like to carry around guilt. Her invitation for anyone in the circle to apologise publicly to individuals for having called them names was enthusiastically taken up. And virtually all hands went up when she asked who was prepared to say they had deliberately wound Justin up. Again, everyone was eager to take turns to be a friend to Justin for a day to help him achieve his agreed aim of getting through the week without losing his temper; and there was no shortage of suggestions for rewarding Justin if he achieved this – applause, a certificate signed by everyone, even an offer to tidy his desk.

'Thank you,' says Justin, 'but I wouldn't know where my stuff was.'

activity

Children's behaviour

1 Think about your own childhood experiences and in a group discuss any positive and negative reinforcements that were used. Debate the issue of smacking and corporal punishment in relation to (a) parental discipline, and (b) teachers and childminders.

2 What greater variety of rewards and punishments can be used on an older child which would not be effective with a younger child?

3 Find out about other techniques for managing behaviour in children:
- contingent reinforcement
- modelling

- shaping
- systematic desensitisation
- response competition
- token economy
- aversion therapy
- social skills training.

Write a brief description of each method. Apply the ABC analysis of behaviour and decide what sorts of behaviour each technique is suited to and with which age groups.

ANXIETY AND WITHDRAWAL

Distress

Distress is the greatest emotional problem for children, and it can manifest itself in many different ways. Nearly all children experience *separation anxiety* when their main carer, usually their mother or father, has to leave them for a while. Also most children have fears of certain things, the most common being fear of spiders, loud noises and water. As children grow older, fear of tangible objects gives way to fear of imaginary and less tangible objects, such as ghosts and 'the dark'.

Phobias

A fear becomes a phobia when it is out of all proportion to the reality of the danger. The difference between a fear and a phobia is that in a phobic disorder, the fear is very intense and there is a compelling desire to avoid the object of the fear. Examples are:

- **agoraphobia** – a fear of public places
- **school phobia** – a morbid fear of going to school
- **arachnophobia** – a fear of spiders
- **aerophobia** – a fear of flying.

Phobias can develop at any time of life; many phobias disappear on their own, but those that persist will only decrease with appropriate psychological treatment.

Eating disorders in childhood and adolescence

The most common eating disorders affecting children and adolescents are obesity, anorexia nervosa and bulimia nervosa. All three have profound implications for the successful development of the individual's self-concept and resulting self-esteem.

Obesity

Obesity or fatness results from taking in more energy from the diet than is used up by the body. Some children appear to inherit a tendency to put on weight very easily, and some parents and carers offer more high-calorie food than children need. Obesity can lead to emotional and social problems as well as the physical problem of being more prone to infections. An obese child is often the target for bullying and, if severely obese, the child will be unable to participate in the same vigorous play as his or her peers.

Anorexia nervosa

Anorexia nervosa is popularly, but wrongly, called the 'slimmer's disease'. Those affected are predominantly adolescent girls from the higher social classes in the developed world, but recent evidence points to problems in children as young as seven years old with a slight increase in the number of boys affected. Features of the disorder are:

- weight loss
- overactivity and obsessive exercising

- amenorrhoea – absence of menstrual periods when otherwise expected to occur
- denial of the seriousness of current low body weight
- tiredness and weakness
- extreme choosiness over food
- lanugo – baby-like hair on body, and thinning of hair on head.

There are various theories on the causes of anorexia:

- Affected individuals do not wish to grow up and are trying to keep their childhood shapes; in part this may be influenced by the media obsession with achieving the 'perfect' (i.e. slim) body and also by the desire to defer the 'storm and stress' of adolescence.
- Those affected see anorexia as a way of taking control over their lives.
- Some specialists see it as a true phobia about putting on weight.
- It may be due to an attempt to avoid adult sexual feelings and behaviours.
- The affected individual is over-involved in her own family so that when she enters adolescence there is a confrontation between the peer group and the family.
- It may be a physical illness caused in part by hormonal changes or a disorder of the hypothalamus (the part of the brain concerned with hunger, thirst and sexual development).
- It may be caused by depression, personality disorder or, rarely, schizophrenia.

Bulimia nervosa

Bulimia is often, but not always, a variant of anorexia nervosa. Again, the majority of individuals affected are female, but recently there has been a rise in the number of males affected. Bulimia nervosa is characterised by episodes of compulsive overeating, usually followed by self-induced vomiting. Features of the disorder include the following:

- the individual may be of normal weight or only slightly underweight
- in severe cases, repeated vomiting leads to dehydration and loss of the body's

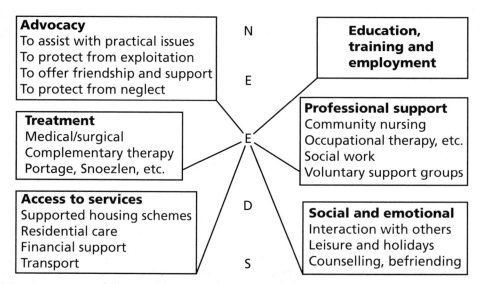

Figure 4.4 A summary of the special needs of people with learning difficulties

vital salts, especially potassium; this may result in weakness and cramps
- the acid present in gastric (stomach) juices may damage tooth enamel
- the individual may become clinically depressed or even suicidal
- bingeing and vomiting may occur once or several times a day
- misuse of laxatives, **diuretics** or other medication is common.

As with anorexia, there is no single cause to account for the disorder. Many of the theories advanced are linked closely to those put forward to explain anorexia nervosa, and include:

- a morbid fear of fatness
- a constant craving for food developed over months or years of crash slimming diets and fasting.

MULTI-HANDICAPPING CONDITIONS

Certain disorders, such as autistic spectrum disorder, may involve combinations of difficulties: there may be severe learning difficulties *and* severe behavioural difficulties. Children who are deaf and blind may have behavioural difficulties *and* severe learning difficulties.

Giftedness

Some educationalists make a distinction between gifted and talented children:

- gifted children being those who are of superior ability over a wide range
- talented children being those who have a specific area of expertise, e.g. musical aptitude or sporting prowess.

There is much debate about whether children who are gifted *do* have special educational needs. Educational approaches include:

- **Enrichment**: the classroom curriculum is specially adapted to support and extend the child's particular abilities.
- **Segregation**: the child is placed in a group of other high ability pupils, who follow a specialised curriculum.
- **Acceleration**: the child is moved up a year in school. This is often the obvious choice, but parents and teachers are now much more aware of the social and emotional effects of separation from the peer group.

Mental illness

As with all health problems, the range of mental health disorders is considerable. They can range from the anxiety and depression which all of us experience from time to time, to serious mental illness which can ruin the lives of individuals and their families.

People with a mental health problem have the same basic needs as anyone else. Often mental illness can affect one's ability to cope with daily life, which can lead to major problems with housing, money and employment. These problems themselves can cause stress and damage morale, which in turn can lead to mental illness or can prevent recovery.

DEPRESSION

Most people experience some degree of depression in response to a personal problem of some kind, or as a reaction to painful events in their lives. Depression may also occur for no apparent reason: this is known as endogenous depression.

It is rare, but not impossible, for very young children to experience depression; in the US about 200 children under the age of 14 commit suicide every year, and some of these are under the age of five (Rosenhan and Seligman, 1989). Children become more vulnerable to depression as they enter adolescence, especially if they are girls. In adulthood, too, women are twice as likely as men to suffer from depression. The characteristics of severe depression include:

- difficulty in making decisions or taking any action that will help relieve the depression
- early morning awakening and other sleep disturbances
- delusions or morbid preoccupations, e.g. of some impending disaster
- extreme misery and possible thoughts of suicide
- loss of appetite and consequent weight loss
- physical slowing and lethargy
- loss of interest and the ability to concentrate
- restlessness and agitation.

Treatment

If the depression is related to social problems and stress, counselling or **psychotherapy** may help. Other treatments include:

- antidepressant drugs
- complementary therapies – such as massage, aromatherapy.
- electro-convulsive therapy (ECT) – a controversial treatment still used for those who do not respond to medication
- self-help groups, e.g. Depressives Anonymous (see 'Useful addresses' section, page 213).

POST-NATAL ILLNESS

After giving birth a woman's hormone levels fluctuate, and this, combined with the physical and emotional exertion of childbirth, can cause new mothers to become weepy and easily upset. In its mild form, it is quite common and is called the 'baby blues'. It is fortunately short-lived and no treatment is required beyond rest and reassurance.

Post-natal depression

This is more serious; it affects about 10 per cent of women and leads to an overwhelming feeling of inadequacy, depressed mood, and loss of energy and interest. Mothers may experience thoughts of self-harm or of harming the baby. The condition can persist for weeks or even months and may require medical treatment in the form of antidepressive drugs.

Puerperal psychosis (or post-natal psychosis)

This is a rare condition, affecting between

1 and 2 mothers per 1,000 births. It is a serious illness with an abrupt onset. The main features of the illness are:

- strong feelings of guilt
- mental confusion
- hallucinations
- delusions and mood disturbances
- strong feelings of despair
- threats of suicide or of harm to the baby

- feelings of worthlessness.

Medical treatment using anti-psychotic drugs is often needed urgently and is normally very successful. Mothers also need counselling and sometimes family therapy. The following case study is a true record of one woman's experience of puerperal psychosis.

CASE STUDY

Puerperal psychosis

I thought I was well prepared for the stresses of labour and childbirth. What I knew nothing about was the possibility of severe mental illness immediately following the birth of a child. I ended up being admitted for psychiatric treatment without my consent ten days after my baby was born.

Let me give you a little background. I was an 'elderly **primigravida**' of 40 whose labour was induced at **term** due to my age. The **induction** proved traumatic for several reasons, although the delivery was normal and my husband and I were thrilled by our baby girl when she arrived.

Almost immediately upon my arrival in the ward just after 6.00 in the morning I did something a little strange. I naturally felt exhausted and wanted the baby taken to the nursery so that I did not have to worry about her. But what I did was ring my bedside buzzer and ask the person who appeared to 'please take the baby away'. At 8.00 breakfast appeared. I attempted to eat, but the spoon slipped out of my

mouth and then I choked on my roll. Fortunately, one of my fellow patients noticed my plight and I was quickly given a glass of water. However this incident preyed on my mind and I remember being disappointed that my morning midwife was not more sympathetic. I suspect I also complained more about my case of piles than was called for, and certainly claimed that I 'could not' sit, even though later when I was required to do so in special care I managed very well. I also had difficulty following the instructions for the baby's care which I was given by the midwife.

As I recall it, the rest of the day was relatively uneventful apart from the fact that my husband's visit was interrupted by the announcement that our house had been burgled. I took this news very calmly and later, when he telephoned the hospital to inform me that nothing had been taken, I laughed about it with the person on duty. What did cause me worry and

contd. ▌▌▌➡

indeed panic that day was a funny feeling that I had while walking down the corridor, as though something had fallen down inside me. I had two theories, both frightening. One was a prolapsed uterus and the other was a stitch falling out – which I was afraid would have to be replaced. I was in such a panic that I delayed asking for advice, and even when I did ask was not able to do so calmly.

The next day, my baby was admitted to the special care baby unit (SCBU) because of jaundice. By this time I was beginning to feel the 'surges' of weakness and energy which later became more obvious. At times I felt so weak I was convinced I was going to lose consciousness. This feeling was particularly evident after breastfeeding. I was transferred to a side ward nearer the SCBU but the bed had no buzzer and was the furthest away from the nursing station. The transfer to my new ward proved very traumatic. My husband had come with me to see the baby taken into special care and we had parted at the lift. I felt too weak and disorientated to get back to the ward, let alone face the idea of feeding the baby every three hours through the night. I progressed back very slowly, clutching the wall as I went and stopping frequently to make sure I was going the right way. Eventually I almost collapsed into the arms of a student midwife who 'took me over' and helped keep me calm by quoting scripture to me on the way to my new bed. My next problem was missing supper while feeding the baby in the SCBU. My bed had no call button and I felt too weak to go and ask for food. When a staff member did come round, I made a play for sympathy and said 'I could

not eat' the sandwiches which were available.

I now began to be preoccupied with the idea of relieving my bowels. Eventually I was given medication to help me, but when I went to the lavatory to see if it had worked, I lost control of my bladder, panicked and pushed the emergency buzzer. I was very upset and incoherent when help arrived.

The next day the baby was well enough to come out of special care. My family came to see us, but when they left I felt bad feelings welling up inside me again, and tried to control them by writing a journal of the day.

2.30. Try to relax. Where are my painkillers? ... Eventually get sorted out after another moan to sister. Comings and goings in ward – feeling weak and down, trying to relax.

During the afternoon the sister visited me, taking time to talk over my problems, and offering to move me to a bed where I could be seen and would have more people to chat to. This helped considerably, but later I started to go out of control again. It is at this point that the writing in my diary began to deteriorate and to slope downward, as I again recalled the contretemps with the night staff over bowel medication. At about 4.00 I began to lose control again, but instead of going to the nursing station to ask about the delay in having the baby checked by special care staff, I picked up the baby and carried her down the corridor. I felt an urgent and overriding desire to know *immediately* that she was all right. This sense of urgency later became an obvious sign of my illness, and usually signalled the beginning of a psychotic episode.

Later that night I woke up feeling ready to feed the baby and recorded in my diary: 'I have been sleeping very well – beautiful deep breath rhythms.' However, this was an unnatural sleep, on my back with my arms spread. I rang to see if the baby was awake and was told she was sleeping and they would let me know when she awoke and was ready for a feed. I slept fitfully and kept waking up and wondering where she was. I got up for a glass of milk and a pee to find the baby being given water by a nurse. I nearly collapsed from shock and anger and a paranoid feeling that the nurses were trying to harm the baby. I felt weak after feeding the baby and was convinced that I had **hypoglycaemia**. I was becoming more and more convinced that the nurses were trying to harm me and the baby. I returned to bed putting a note into the baby's cot which said in large letters: 'PLEASE DO NOT TAKE MY BABY AWAY!'

I found myself shaking again, decided to try to act rationally and ring to tell the staff I would keep the baby for the rest of the night, and to request more milk. This was refused because I had already had three glasses. 'Feel I'm about to go comatose.' I insisted I had hypoglycaemia and asked for a doctor, trying 'please, please', holding on to the nurse, but then began shouting and screaming. The nurse tested my blood sugar level, which was normal, but I did not believe her. By the time the doctor arrived I was able to explain my symptoms but did not believe the doctor's diagnosis 'nothing serious' or his advice to try to rest. I didn't relax, but instead began trying to organise myself

and the hospital for my exit, determined that I would not spend another night with that night staff.

The day passed relatively uneventfully. I was pleased that I had at last received all the meals that I had ordered. However, the exit procedure proved to be complicated and time-consuming, and during a time when I was left alone, I began to panic. When I asked a student nurse who was passing to take my blood pressure, she visibly jumped, and tried again. It was raised. 'Don't panic,' I wrote, 'and always take a towel.'

The other event of the day was an **enema**. I felt I could not return home unless my bowels were back in working order. My gratitude at the success of the treatment was boundless! I could not thank the sister enough times or at enough length – I had to announce it to others as well! In addition, I spent time doing things for others, giving presents, etc. I could not seem to rest even when there was an opportunity.

At last the moment we were waiting for arrived – at 7 p.m. we were told, 'Your papers are ready; you can go any time you like.' So off we went – it had not occurred to any of us that we had to do anything with the said papers. Suddenly, while we were waiting for our taxi, two staff members came running downstairs after us. By this time I was rigid with fear and could not speak coherently. I asked the student if she would be a witness for me, and heard her say I would need plenty of witnesses. My sister had been told by the sister in charge on the last day (she who gave me the blessed enema) to watch for signs of any strange or unusual behaviour, but the

contd. ▮▮▮➡

only name she had to pin on it was 'post-natal depression'. Neither myself nor my husband were given any information or any warning that my behaviour might be unusual or indicative of any problem. I felt that I had coped with 'an inordinate level of stress', and later on that 'I'm a case study for the medical world in how to cope with post-natal depression and stress and therefore to lower the infant mortality rate in . . .'

Four days later, after the energy surges and faintness panics, the broken sleep patterns, and the tirades against hospital staff had worn my family down so that they could no longer cope, my baby and I were admitted to the acute psychiatric ward of the same hospital. Fortunately, there was a mother and baby unit available, so that her presence helped me to recover quickly. Luckier still, my employer had a private health plan which enabled me to come home after eight days and be attended at home by a private nurse until I was well enough to cope again.

I cannot help thinking and feeling that things might have been different if we had only known something about the illness before it became so serious, and that hospital staff should have recognised at least some of the early signs and passed them on in an appropriate fashion. I recognise that that cannot be changed, and hope that by reading part of my story it may help hospital staff somewhere to do better for some other sufferer(s) from puerperal psychosis.

activity

Research into mental illness

1 Find out about the different kinds of depression: exogenous or reactive depression; endogenous depression; manic depression. What help is available for people who experience depression?

2 The mother who wrote the record in the case study above of her own experience of puerperal psychosis has needed anti-psychotic medication for many years since the birth of her only child. List the signs and symptoms that should have alerted the medical and nursing staff to her problems.

3 What is schizophrenia? Find out about the different therapies available for people with schizophrenia:
- cognitive therapy
- gestalt therapy
- primal therapy
- behavioural therapy
- bioenergetics
- hypnotherapy.

DEMENTIA

Dementia is a term used to describe all illnesses which cause a progressive loss of mental function. People with dementia usually show the following characteristics:

- reduced abilities to think and to reason logically
- impaired memory for people, events or even where they are
- difficulty in thinking abstractly
- personality changes.

The most common cause of dementia is Alzheimer's disease or pre-senile dementia. There are at least eight other forms of dementia. Second in frequency to Alzheimer's disease is multi-infarct dementia, which arises following a series of small strokes. Blood supply to part of the brain is cut off, and if the areas killed are essential for thinking and remembering, the result is dementia. Dementia can also occur in people with advanced Parkinson's disease, as important nerves are destroyed by the illness. About 15 per cent of people infected by the human immunodeficiency virus (HIV), which causes AIDS, suffer from poor memory and concentration, typical of dementia. Creutzfeldt-Jakob disease (CJD) is a rare cause of dementia which was once only seen in elderly people. Recently a new form of CJD has been linked to infection with an agent called a prion, found in cattle with bovine spongiform encephalopathy (BSE). This agent has been identified in at least 10 people who contracted the disease at an unusually young age. It is this form of the disease that scientists believe may be caused by eating infected beef.

Alzheimer's disease

Alzheimer's disease is associated with old age, affecting 1 in 20 people aged over 65 and 1 in 5 of those over 80. It is not, however, always confined to the elderly; it can affect people as young as 40.

The disease was first described in 1907, by a German doctor called Alois Alzheimer. He used a newly invented technique of straining slices of brain tissue to study the brain of a 51-year-old woman who had died after experiencing memory loss and personality changes in the last few years of her life. Her brain contained many dark spots, not normally found in healthy brain tissue, and Dr Alzheimer believed that these caused the changes in behaviour. These dark spots are now called senile plaques and neurofibrillary tangles. In Alzheimer's disease these senile plaques interfere with the transmission of the signal from one neurone to another and the neurofibrillary tangles prevent the transport of essential chemicals within the cell body.

What causes Alzheimer's disease?

No one knows what causes Alzheimer's disease, but there are many theories.

- **A genetic link**: some families suffer from Alzheimer's disease more than others, suggesting that they might have genes that predispose them to it. This is particularly evident in people who develop the disease in middle age.
- **A deficit in the neurotransmitter acetylcholine**: research is under way to find a drug that will correct this problem.
- **A slow-working virus**: the Alzheimer's virus lies dormant in most people until genes or life experiences somehow activate it in some people later in life.
- **An accumulation of aluminium in the brain**: the controversial theory that exposure to aluminium, a metal which is very abundant in nature, may cause

Alzheimer's disease is now disputed; it is likely that aluminium is only one of the environmental factors that may cause or accelerate the progress of the disease.

● **A group of distinct diseases**, each with a different cause.

● **A faulty gene (on chromosome 21)**: this makes affected individuals produce an abnormal form of amyloid protein, which is deposited in the nerves and blood vessel walls of the brain. The fact that people with Down's syndrome – caused by an extra copy of chromosome 21 – are prone to Alzheimer's disease supports the idea that amyloid protein is responsible.

Diagnosis

Making a diagnosis of Alzheimer's disease, rather than any other dementia, is difficult. Diagnosis is carried out by eliminating other possible disorders and can only be finally confirmed once the person has died, when parts of their brain can be examined under a microscope to look for the characteristic plaques.

Features of Alzheimer's disease

The first symptoms of Alzheimer's disease may at first be confused with forgetfulness or depression. It is often only when the changes in behaviour start to affect someone else that the disease is noticed. Some of the more usual features of the disease are:

● listlessness and apathy
● meaningless but obsessive rituals, e.g. touching door knobs
● regularly forgetting incidents that have just happened

Figure 4.5 Alzheimer's disease poster

● distracted behaviour that has no apparent reason
● slowing down of thought processes
● impaired judgement, e.g. inability to judge distance, speed or hazards when driving
● anti-social behaviour, e.g. shoplifting
● uninhibited sexual behaviour, e.g. stripping off clothes in a crowded street.

In the latter stages of the disease, there may be complete disorientation, loss of verbal abilities and incontinence. Eventually, the person will become incapable of caring for him or herself and may start wandering, especially at night.

CASE STUDY

Alzheimer's disease

Lily, at 59 years old, had always seemed to enjoy good health. Her three children were all grown up with families of their own, and Lily worked in the local sixth form college in the student support office. She enjoyed sorting out the problems encountered in the college – making sure students were registered on the right course, organising student interviews and liaising with other staff. Recently, however, Lily's colleagues had noticed that she was often rather 'distant' and didn't keep up to date with the routine daily tasks.

Lily's husband, John, worked as a buyer for a large retail chain store; he was often away from home, so Lily's increasingly abnormal behaviour was not apparent for a few months. One day he noticed that Lily seemed rather 'down' and asked her if she would like to visit their eldest daughter for a holiday. Lily agreed, but later that evening she had completely forgotten his suggestion and was talking of different holiday plans. When John reminded her of their plans, she looked a little worried and said that she simply didn't remember. When John and Lily were relaxing in front of the TV one evening, John suddenly smelled smoke. Lily had put a saucepan of soup on the stove but had forgotten to watch it. John reminded her that they had already eaten a meal only one hour previously, but Lily could not remember putting on the soup or why she might have done so. In fact, she became really angry and started accusing John of making things up

or of being hypercritical of everything she did.

Eventually, as Lily approached her sixtieth birthday, she was called in to see her manager at the college. They told her that as she was nearing retirement age, she should be prepared to leave that year. Lily seemed not to be aware that her colleagues had more or less taken over the tasks that she had previously fulfilled so competently; she agreed that she was looking forward to retirement and, after a small farewell party, Lily went home to organise her future.

John became increasingly worried about the changes he saw in his wife. He invited their son, Kenneth, to visit. Kenneth was a nurse at a large district general hospital. He was dismayed by the changes he observed in his mother and suggested that she see her GP. Fortunately, Kenneth was able to accompany Lily on this first visit, so the GP could ascertain the true extent of the changes in behaviour. Arrangements were made for a CT scan to be carried out. This scan revealed that Lily's brain had shrunk considerably in size, and a diagnosis of Alzheimer's disease was reached.

Lily seemed to deteriorate very rapidly once she was diagnosed, although the two things did not seem to be related. John was afraid to go to work in case Lily wandered off and then forgot her way home. One day, he had just returned from a trip to Scotland and could not find Lily

contd. ❚❚❚➡

anywhere. He called all their friends and family, but nobody had seen her. Just as John was about to call the police, Lily turned up. She appeared very miserable, was unable to account for the past 24 hours, and said, 'I just want to go to sleep.'

John realised that the problem was becoming worse almost daily. He was anxious every time he had to go away on business. Only the week before, on a very hot day, he had had to throw out a whole week's shopping because Lily had forgotten to put perishable items in the fridge and freezer. The next day, he received a call from the security staff at the local garden centre to say that Lily was sitting on the floor in the showroom, rocking backwards and forwards and chanting. He asked his family to come together to try to arrange some sort of long-term care for Lily. Lily was now no longer the same person who was mother to Kenneth, Helen and Rosemary; she was no longer the Lily who had married John and lived with him for 35 years. She muttered to herself continually. She believed that everyone was

against her. She had started to wander off in the night. She had no insight into her problems and became very anxious if she was faced with any new situations or with meeting new people.

Kenneth contacted the local Alzheimer's Disease Society, which offers advice on practical, financial and emotional issues relating to the disease and its effects on the people who care for those with dementia. Their advice was to try to keep to a set routine and to try to avoid unnecessary anxiety. Often, when Alzheimer's disease strikes, relatives decide to move house, considering options such as a bungalow or sheltered housing. Most experts advise against this as new surroundings can make Alzheimer's sufferers unduly anxious because they cannot retain *existing* information, let alone absorb new information. The home environment should be kept as familiar as possible and when the person with Alzheimer's disease feels anxious about ordinary or everyday tasks, he or she should be persuaded to allow someone else to take responsibility.

The Alzheimer's Disease Society produces a pamphlet which offers useful advice to anyone looking after a relative showing signs of developing Alzheimer's disease (see Figure 4.6).

activity

Assessing needs

1 Read the case study and the guidelines for care produced by the Alzheimer's Disease Society in Figure 4.6. As a group, discuss what measures Lily's family could take to ensure the best possible care for Lily.

(a) List the activities of daily living (see page 12) which may present problems for Lily both now and in the future.

Memory, Thinking & Conversation

☐ Remember the importance of good communication. Ensure that hearing aids, glasses and dentures are in place and working.

☐ Speak clearly, slowly and simply.

☐ Use body language (touch, and so on) to help communicate. People with dementia are often surprisingly sensitive to this.

☐ Make sure that clocks, calendars and room signs are easily seen. Four clocks all telling a different time would confuse anyone. One clock with the correct time is all that is necessary.

☐ Draw attention to these memory aids.

☐ When you are talking about the past don't confuse it with the present.

☐ Try to avoid reinforcing confused behaviour. Sometimes it is best to ignore the behaviour or to change the subject. If it seems necessary, correct it tactfully. You may be able to pacify the person, without going along with confused thinking, by saying something like "I can't see anyone in the room, but I know you can and it must be very upsetting for you." This acknowledges the fear without going along with the confusion.

☐ Deal with repeated questions with as much tact and patience as you can.

☐ Tell the person what is going on and what is happening next. Repeat this if necessary.

☐ As far as possible let the person do what they enjoy doing.

General Appearance, Hygiene & Dressing

☐ Some people with dementia need reminding about hygiene as they simply forget whether they have bathed or shaved.

☐ Even if the person cannot carry out the whole task alone allow them to do what they can. Take things a step at a time.

☐ For safety reasons some supervision of bathing and shaving is desirable. Make the occasion as pleasant as possible.

☐ Use bath aids. Contact the social work department of the health authority.

☐ Compliment the person on his or her clean and tidy appearance.

☐ A visit to the hairdresser can be a morale boost.

☐ Select clothes which the person likes wearing.

☐ Lay out clean clothes in the order that they are put on.

☐ Remove from sight any clothes for washing.

☐ Simplify clothing. Use slip-on shoes, replace buttons and zips with velcro.

Alzheimer's Disease Society
Caring for Dementia

Wandering

Wandering constantly from one place to another with no apparent purpose is very common in people who are confused. This may be partly the result of confusion and partly lack of stimulation.

☐ Try distracting and coaxing the person rather than confronting them.

☐ If the person wanders a lot install locks that are difficult to operate.

☐ A lock at the bottom of the door, where they are less likely to look for it, can be effective.

☐ Even with precautions wandering may continue. Try to tolerate it.

☐ Have an identity bracelet made for the person. Do not have the address printed on it. A name and telephone number are sufficient.

Aggression

☐ Try not to interpret the anger as if it were coming from a healthy person. Anger from someone with dementia is often exaggerated.

☐ Keep calm. Anger may be intensified if you respond angrily. Count to ten (or twenty) before saying anything, and then try to distract the person.

☐ Remember that forgetfulness is an advantage in these situations. Once the outburst is over the person will usually forget what has happened.

☐ Try to avoid touchy subjects.

Health and Safety

As the person's ability to reason and remember declines, everyday situations become a potential hazard. It is often difficult to decide how far to restrict their freedom in order to prevent risks. You cannot remove all the dangers.

☐ Check the house for hazards such as trailing wires, faulty electrical appliances, access to gas appliances, loose rugs and low glass tables. Make sure medicines, cleaning fluids, paint and bleach are all out of reach.

☐ Looking after someone with dementia is exhausting. You must take care of yourself and work out some survival strategies.

☐ Don't keep the problem a secret. Tell those close to you so that you can share it. Dementia is a distressing illness but also a common one. People may understand and sympathise more than you expect.

☐ You are an individual with interests and needs of your own. Try to retain old acquaintances and spend time with them. This may mean taking time off from caring. There may be a day centre or sitting service in your area.

☐ Try to 'switch off' at home when things get on top of you. Go to another room and read or just sit alone for a short time. The person you are caring for will probably not notice your absence and you will feel better.

☐ Consider joining a self-help group where you will meet other people in the same position.

☐ Be prepared to accept that there comes a point at which you can no longer cope and admission to hospital or residential care is necessary.

Figure 4.6 Excerpts from the Alzheimer's Society leaflet

(b) For each activity, suggest a possible solution.

2 Find out what services are available to help people with Alzheimer's disease and other forms of dementia in your area. List these services under two headings: *statutory services* and *voluntary services*. Compile a booklet which contains useful information about the options available for people with dementia in your area, including contact addresses and telephone numbers.

Drug dependence

A drug is any chemical substance which changes the function of one or more body organs or alters the process of a disease. Drugs may be:

- prescribed medicines
- over-the-counter remedies
- alcohol, tobacco and caffeine
- illegal drugs.

Drug abuse is the use of a drug for a purpose other than that for which it is normally prescribed. *Drug dependence* is the compulsion to continue taking a drug. There are two types of drug dependence.

1 **psychological** – the person experiences craving or emotional distress when the drug is withdrawn

Figure 4.7 Why do people take drugs?

2 **physical** – the body has adapted to the presence of the drug and symptoms of withdrawal syndrome are caused when the drug is withdrawn.

People start to take drugs for many different reasons (see Figure 4.7).

CASE STUDY

Substance abuse

Certain drugs are more fashionable than others; the 1960s saw a surge of cannabis use and the 1980s saw the advent of ecstasy use. The Kaleidoscope Project in Kingston upon Thames is a sanctuary for people who are dependent on drugs. In their first magazine, called *The Scope*, an 18-year-old man, Robert, talks of his experiences.

'Dance drugs can really mess you up. They are not physically addictive, but they can lead to mental addiction. I was mentally addicted. I was not just doing them at music events, I was doing them every day. They made me lose weight and I started to deal to keep my habit. I did my first wrap of speed when I was 13. I was at an under-18 disco. I was offered some, and thought I would try it. It gave me a new sense of alertness. It made me want to dance all night. It made me forget everything that was happening in my life.

I was at a foster home at the time. My foster dad would not let me go to the disco so I nicked some money out of his wallet and went anyway. Why do you take dance drugs? Because when you go to a club and do drugs you can do things you would not be able to do when you're straight. If you were a shy person you would no longer be. On the drug, you would just run up to someone and introduce yourself. You lose all your inhibitions. There is a big group of ravers that goes to all the raves. The industry is huge. If you went to a rave and found more than the odd person not on a drug, I'd give you a tenner. Obviously some people don't do drugs – but not many. I would say 2 in every 10 people are beerheads. They get pissed and get into fights. People on dance drugs can be a problem but they hardly ever fight. They are so loved up with the world they tend to just walk away from people who want to fight.

I know these drugs can kill, because I've seen it happen. I was talking to a geezer called Ben for two or three hours in a club. He was fine when he left me. A couple of hours later he was found dead in the toilet.

It took me a long time to admit that I had a drug problem. Now my life is much better. I can talk to my case manager at Kaleidoscope. I have stopped taking drugs and am doing an NVQ in health and social care. I would like to become a social or youth worker. I feel I would be good at that because I know the system and would understand what young people are going through. Too many people are prejudiced against people who take drugs, so how can they help them go straight?'

Don't storm, inform

Dance drugs are here to stay. They are as much part of youth culture as dance music. Police storming nightclubs heightens paranoia, but does little to discourage use. Hundreds of thousands of clubbers take drugs. The question is no longer how to stop them, but how to help young people make an informed choice about their use. The Acid House movement of 1988, the so-called Second Summer of Love, changed youth culture dramatically. With it came 3,4 methylenedioxymethamphetamine: Ecstasy.

E, or MDMA, was originally synthesised by German pharmacist E. Merck in 1911. It was used for repressing the appetites of German soldiers in World War II. American Dr Alexander Shulgin re-engineered MDMA and it hit the streets of Britain as the 'love drug'.

E can be dangerous but death and prosecution no longer deter. Over 50 people have died from the after-effects of ecstasy since the 1980s, including, of course, Leah Betts. Tragic as these deaths have been, soaring consumption of ecstasy demonstrates that the 'Just say no' campaign of the 1980s has flopped. A lot of ecstasy dealing in clubs is controlled by the management, usually through bouncers. Money, not clubbers' safety, tends to be at the top of their agenda. For example, water, which clubbers need to rehydrate, costs more than £1 for a small bottle. Why? Because, instead of getting 'beered up' most clients now take E, so bar takings drop.

In 1992 the Manchester drug agency, Lifeline, drew up guidelines for clubs. These included providing first aid cover; limiting admission and controlling safety; providing adequate ventilation; providing 'chill out' areas and free cold water; regulating the rhythm of music and strobe lighting.

Release, the London-based help group, has built on this approach with its Dance Information network. Club managers, drug workers and police are brought together to discuss health promotion strategies.

Health information, with its overtones of censure, is giving way to health promotion. This more realistic approach should now be coupled with a crackdown on unsafe clubs.

The Scope

activity

The most commonly abused drugs in the UK are alcohol and tobacco. These drugs do cause dependency, but it is legal for adults to buy and consume them. List the special needs of someone who is dependent on the following substances:

- heroin
- solvents (as in glue sniffing)
- cocaine and crack
- ecstasy
- alcohol.

For each substance, describe:

- the legal situation concerning the sale and use of the substance
- the effects on the individual user of long-term abuse and dependence
- the support, both practical and psychological, available to the individual in your local area.

Homelessness

Homelessness in the UK is not the result of a national disaster like a flood or a famine, it is primarily a failure of the housing system. There is simply not enough housing that people can afford. Housing is one of the basic needs for survival and there is a close relationship between health and housing. A study of homeless people in overnight hostels claimed that one in four people who are homeless suffer from schizophrenia (Brandon, 1980). A common distinction is often made between single homeless people and homeless people with dependent children, or homeless families.

The factors triggering homelessness include:

- a relationship breakdown, particularly a breakdown in parental relationships
- the loss of an owner-occupied home
- eviction from a privately rented home
- a background in local authority care – while 1 per cent of young people in the UK are in local authority care, 34 per cent of London runaways had run there from care
- domestic violence and child abuse
- the drift into homelessness from institutional life, in particular from psychiatric hospitals.

The underlying explanations for homelessness in the UK centre around:

- job loss and insecurity
- reduced entitlement to state benefits
- shortage of owner-occupied and rented housing for poorer sections of the community
- repossession as a result of mortgage payment arrears.

LOCAL AUTHORITIES' LEGAL DUTIES TOWARDS HOMELESS PEOPLE

Under the Housing Act 1985, all local authorities have a legal duty to provide accommodation for certain people who are homeless. Once someone has been officially classified as homeless they will generally be offered temporary housing, which may be bed and breakfast, until a suitable permanent property becomes available. Some authorities now also operate schemes which help people to find private rented housing. People are accepted as homeless if they are classed as *both* unintentionally homeless (or threatened with homelessness) and in priority need.

Unintentionally homeless or threatened with homelessness

A person will fall into this category if, for example, a landlord or the person's parents have asked them to leave or if they are subject to violence where they are living. The local housing department will require proof of the situation and may also contact a previous address to see if it is possible to return there. Help will not be provided if the person has done something deliberately in order to apply for housing as a homeless person, e.g. deliberately withholding the rent so that eviction follows.

Priority need

This covers:

- families with children
- women expecting a baby
- people over 60
- people who are vulnerable because of mental illness, physical disability or other special reason
- those made homeless through fire, flood or other disaster.

Again, proof of need is essential, such as a letter from a doctor or a social worker. If the applicant is in priority need but is intentionally homeless, the duty is to provide only temporary accommodation for a limited period and advice and assistance in finding housing. If the applicant is not a priority need, the authority only has a duty to provide advice and assistance to them in finding their own accommodation.

YOUTH HOMELESSNESS

Every year, as many as 40,000 children in the UK run away from home or from insti-

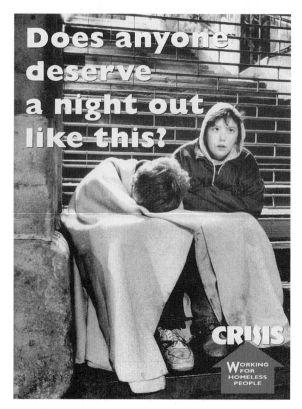

Figure 4.8   Homeless people

tutional care. Brandon *et al.* (1980) outlined five models for explaining homelessness:

- the political model
- the individual culpability model
- the pathological model
- the child model
- the spiritual/religious model.

The political model

Homelessness stems from the structure of society, rather than from an individual's actions or behaviour. The most important factors are issues such as the housing market, the labour market and the state benefits system. One disadvantage of the political model is that, in focusing on the structures and systems of society, the individual homeless person may be viewed as powerless and incapable of self-determination. As with the medical model of disability, the individual person and his or her needs are defined by the wider social structures, thus creating powerless victims.

The individual culpability model

This model sees youth homelessness as a consequence of the individual behaviour of young homeless people themselves; it has little or nothing to do with social structures. It apportions blame for the condition of homelessness directly to the young person. The argument runs: 'Young homeless people do not *have* to leave home. They do not *have* to engage in crime or substance abuse. As individuals in a free society, they have a choice and they are responsible for whatever decision they make.'

The pathological model

This model also sees the causes of homelessness as individually based, but does not hold the individual as directly responsible. It sees the behaviour of the individual as a consequence of individual pathologies, which probably result from factors such as child abuse or an experience in care. Although this model acknowledges the influence of social structures in aggravating problems, it can lead

to young people being stigmatised. They may be seen as a 'special group' needing specialist support when perhaps their only problem is lack of accommodation.

The child model

Youth homelessness stems from the fact that many young homeless people are simply too immature. It identifies homelessness as being an individually based problem rather than a structural one. The child model takes into account the problems caused by inadequate social structures, but views the young person as being too vulnerable, naive and immature to be able to cope with them. The young homeless person may feel patronised, but the model avoids stigmatising the individual as somehow abnormal or pathological.

The spiritual/religious model

This model sees homelessness as a fall from grace which could happen to anybody. It is related not so much to social or economic privation, but to the spiritual poverty of society in general. A society which does not adopt the Christian values of compassion and caring suffers from spiritual poverty. It is not enough to improve the material provision for homelessness; the main task is to improve the spiritual content of both society and homeless people. Many homelessness agencies started out with this perspective in mind, but it is now out of favour.

activity

Divide into groups of three or four and prepare a fact-file on homelessness.

Stage 1

Describe the special needs of homeless people, arising from problems such as:

- poor or non-existent access to health services
- food poisoning
- infestation by parasites
- stress-related illnesses
- high accident rates
- nutritional difficulties
- high infection rates
- emotional insecurity.

Stage 2

Find out about the work done by voluntary organisations to meet the needs of homeless people – examples include SHELTER, Barnardos, The Salvation Army, Cyreneans, Centrepoint and the Campaign for Homeless and Rootless (CHAR).

Stage 3

(a) What do homeless people *themselves* think could be done to tackle the problem of youth homelessness, particularly street sleeping in cities? Find out by looking at *The Big Issue*, a publication sold in many cities in the UK which gives homeless people a chance to express their own views.

(b) What do you think are the main effects of homelessness on people's everyday lives, and what do you think could be done to minimise the problems of homelessness?

Stage 4

Research the provision for single homeless people and homeless families in your local area. In particular, find out about housing associations, bed and breakfast accommodation, hostels, night shelters, drop-in centres and outreach work.

Child abuse

Child abuse is a painful subject, but one about which it is important that all people working with children should know. The abuse of children by adults has been carried out for centuries. It is only in the past few decades that the media has high-lighted the nature of the problem and public concern has increased. The Children Act 1989 places a duty on the local authorities to undertake child protection work to find out which children are at risk by keeping child protection registers; a central register is also maintained by the National Council for the Prevention of Cruelty to Children (NSPCC).

There have been various theories about why adults abuse or neglect children:

- All sections and social classes of society produce adults who abuse or neglect children. It is very dangerous to stereotype either the kind of people who might harm children or the situations which might lead to child abuse or neglect.
- The abusive or neglectful adult is almost always known to the child, e.g. a parent, a family member, a friend of the family or a carer.
- Premature babies and children under the age of four years are most likely to be abused or neglected.
- Children who cry a great deal are much more likely to be abused or neglected.
- Children who do not enjoy eating are more likely to be abused or neglected.
- Step-children are vulnerable.
- Disabled children are more likely to be abused or neglected.

- Children who are separated from their mother for some period following their birth are more likely to be abused or neglected.

PHYSICAL ABUSE

Physical abuse – also called non-accidental injury (NAI) – involves someone deliberately harming a child. It may take the form of:

- bruising – from being slapped, shaken, squeezed or punched
- cuts, scratches, bite marks, torn frenulum (the web of skin inside the upper lip)
- burns and scalds
- fractures
- poisoning.

Anyone who works with children should be aware of the indicators of physical abuse (see Figure 4.9). Although it is important not to jump to conclusions, any concerns that you may have about the nature of an injury should be dealt with

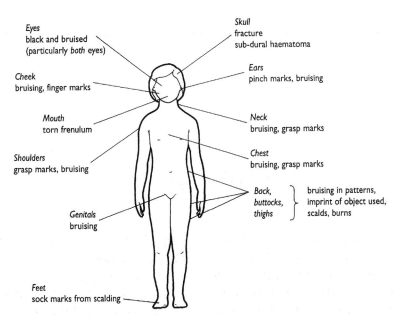

Figure 4.9 Non-accidental injury indicators

according to the procedures outlined below. Usually the explanation of the parent or carer of how the injury occurred is inadequate and their attitude may be bizarre. The parents may have delayed seeking medical help or only done so when prompted by others.

A child who has been physically abused may:

- appear fearful or apprehensive when other children cry
- be unusually withdrawn or aggressive
- have an air of 'frozen watchfulness'; the child is very alert, constantly looking around, but passive and wary of adults
- report injury
- show fear of parents.

Head injuries

If a baby or young child is shaken very hard or hit against a hard surface, there is a danger of brain injury, which can cause permanent brain damage and even lead to death. The soft brain, which does not yet fit snugly into the skull, can be damaged by crashing against the skull bones; this can cause bleeding into the brain (subdural haematoma).

PHYSICAL NEGLECT

Physical neglect occurs when an adult fails to give a child what he or she needs to develop physically: the child is frequently left alone and unattended, and does not have adequate food, sleep, clothing, clean environments, warmth, supervision or medical care. Extreme neglect usually involves an element of emotional neglect as well. It includes exposure to any kind of danger which results in serious damage to the child's health and development.

Children who are neglected usually

show obvious outward signs, and may also show behavioural problems related to physical and emotional deprivation:

- they may be underweight and show other signs of **failure to thrive**
- their clothing may be inappropriate for the weather and be smelly and dirty
- they may have poor skin tone and dull matted hair; a baby may have a persistent rash from infrequent nappy changing
- they may be constantly hungry, tired and listless
- they may have frequent health problems and be prone to accidents
- they may have low self-esteem, poor social relationships and an air of 'frozen watchfulness'
- delay in all developmental areas is likely, due to lack of stimulation.

The causes of physical neglect are very complex, but the main feature is of children being left unsupervised – or inadequately supervised – at home. Children who are neglected in this way are frequently injured in accidents, both in their own homes and on the roads where they play.

EMOTIONAL ABUSE AND NEGLECT

Emotional abuse occurs when children are threatened by the adult; they are shouted at and constantly ridiculed. *Emotional neglect* occurs when children are not given love and affection by the adult; they are often left alone without the support and company of someone who loves them.

Children who are emotionally abused or neglected may:

- become withdrawn

Non-accidental injuries	Accidental injuries

Bruises
Likely to be:
    in a regular pattern
    of various ages
    reflecting the shape of the object used –
    e.g. belt, buckle, teeth marks etc.
    on lips and mouth due to forced feeding
    with a bottle
	Bruises
	Likely to be:
	    few but scattered
	    no pattern
	    of the same colour and age
	    N.B. may be confused with *mongolian spot* (smooth bluish-grey patches seen on the buttocks of some children of African or Asian origin in infancy)

Cuts and abrasions
Suspicious if:
    large, deep scratches
    bite marks and fingernail marks
    torn frenulum web of skin inside
    upper lip
    incisions e.g. from a razor blade
	Cuts and abrasions
	Likely to be:
	    minor and superficial
	    easily explained
	    treated

Burns and scalds
Likely to have:
    a clear outline – splash marks around
    the burn area
    an unusual position – e.g. back of hand,
    palms or buttocks
    immersion scalds – on buttocks or
    socks area
    the shape of the object used –
    e.g. an iron or a cigarette
	Burns and scalds
	Likely to be:
	    easily explained
	    treated
	    confused with severe nappy rash or
	    impetigo

Fractures
Likely to be:
    numerous – in various stages of healing
    to the skull, nose and face
    very rare in very young babies
    a delay in seeking treatment
	Fractures
	Likely to be:
	    of arms and legs
	    seldom on ribs except with road
	    traffic accidents
	    due (though rarely) to 'brittle bone
	    syndrome'

Table 4.3   Comparison of non-accidental injuries with accidental injuries

- be unable to take part in everyday play or generally to have fun
- tell lies
- have speech disorders, e.g. stammering
- have low self-esteem
- show a lack of self-confidence
- seek attention
- have temper tantrums past the age when they are part of normal development.

SEXUAL ABUSE

Sexual abuse occurs when an adult uses a child in order to gratify his or her sexual needs. This could involve sexual intercourse or anal intercourse. It may involve watching pornographic material (e.g. films or magazines) with the child. Sexual abuse might mean children being encouraged in sexually explicit behaviour or oral sex, masturbation or the handling of sexual parts. Ten per cent of sexual abusers are women. Children who are sexually abused can be both boys and girls.

Sexually abused children feel betrayed and respond to being used as a sexual object. They feel spoiled, debased and violated. Bewildering feelings of guilt are mixed with anger and shame. This form of abuse can continue undetected for some years and will result in the child having poor self-esteem.

Physical indicators of sexual abuse:
- bruises or scratches inconsistent with accidental injury
- difficulty in sitting or walking
- sleep disturbances and bed-wetting
- pain or itching in the genital area; discharges from the vagina or penis
- underclothes may be blood-stained or torn
- loss of appetite.

Behavioural indicators of sexual abuse:

- lack of self-confidence
- poor self-esteem
- may flirt with adults as if trying to please
- withdrawn from other children and some adults
- fascination with sexual behaviour
- use of explicit sexual language .
- unusual amount of knowledge about sexual behaviour shown through work, play, drawings, etc.
- poor sleep patterns.

THE ABUSE OF DISABLED CHILDREN

Children with a physical or learning difficulty are especially vulnerable to all kinds of abuse; some children are abused by the people who care for them, while others are victims to society's view of disabled people as an 'inferior' minority group. The following factors increase their vulnerability to abuse:

- Dependency on others for care may result in an increased desire to please and a need for affection.
- The abuser may be especially attracted to the child's immature behaviour, which is less threatening than adult interaction.
- The abuser may feel it is safer to abuse a child with a disability; the child is less able to disclose or report the abuse because of social isolation, difficulty in communication or lack of understanding.
- Some characteristics, such as poor feeding and sleeping patterns, constant crying or aggression, may provoke physical, emotional or sexual abuse.
- Children in institutional care may be victims of institutionalised abuse; lack of staff and other resources may lead to

harsh punishment techniques or severe lack of stimulation.

- Information about abuse is less likely to be offered to disabled children.

GUIDELINES FOR CARE

If a child tells you that he or she has been abused:

- Reassure the child. Show respect and tell the child that you are pleased he or she has told you about this.
- Listen carefully. Don't prompt the child or ask leading questions.
- Believe the child. Show the child that you are taking the matter seriously and say that you will do your best to help.
- Let the child set the pace and only ask open-ended questions. Stop the conversation as soon as the child wishes.
- Report your conversation with the child to your senior designated manager.

If you are caring for a child and notice indicators of any form of abuse or neglect:

- Be observant. If you are uneasy about any aspects of behaviour or physical signs, make a note of your observations.
- Try to involve the child in play activities, particularly activities that will allow for the release of emotions and will help to build self-esteem.
- Report your suspicions to your senior designated manager.
- Be aware of what is normal development in children's behaviour; for example, most children have a curiosity about going to the toilet and are interested in their bodies.

Abuse of adults and elderly people

People with severe disabilities and frail elderly people who need care at home or in an institution are also at risk of abuse from those who care for them. It is impossible to gauge the extent of this problem. As with the abuse of children, it can take different forms: physical abuse, neglect, emotional abuse and sexual abuse. People who enter a caring profession must be aware of the indicators of abuse and watch out for symptoms of stress shown by the carers (see page 165). A recent report on the abuse of elderly people called *Hearing the Despair: The Reality of Elder Abuse* explodes the myth that the stressed carer is the abuser. The report evaluated a helpline set up specifically to log incidents of elder abuse; it found that in only 5 per cent of cases were older people abused by the person mainly responsible for looking after them. Relatives were the most likely to be guilty of abuse in 41 per cent of cases, followed by paid workers at 26 per cent and friends or neighbours at 16 per cent. The report also found that 20 per cent of incidents took place in nursing homes, compared with 70 per cent taking place in elderly people's own homes. Many callers to the telephone helpline expressed despair; elderly people were suffering but felt unable or too frightened to change their situations.

RESOURCES

Down's syndrome

Student information

Down's Syndrome: Your Questions Answered by Mary Sawtell (DSA, 1995)
Working with People with a Learning Disability (Mencap, 1993)

Videos

One of us
   This 12-minute video focuses on three families with a child with Down's syndrome talking about their feelings and the future.

Education: Preparation for Life
   This 15-minute video shows aspects of the education of four children with Down's syndrome in four different schools.

Books

Down's syndrome by Dr Richard Newton
Published by Optima (1992)

Children with Special Needs by Richard Woolfson
Published by Faber & Faber (1991)
   The resources listed above are all obtainable from the *Down's Syndrome Association* (see 'Useful addresses' section on page 213).
   A video detailing the story retold on page 26 about Joanne Harris is available from Channel 4 videos: *A Heart for Jo* (first screened on 22 August 1996).

Autism

Videos

Rain Man
A Warner Home Video (1988)
   In the film, Charlie Babbitt discovers he has an older brother with autism who has been living away from home for many years.

Autism: A World Apart
   This video provides an overview of autism, and the stress on families of having a child with autism, and looks at some of the services available. It can be obtained from the National Autistic Society (see 'Useful addresses', page 213).

Books about autism

Autism by Laura Schreibman
Published by Sage Publications (1998)

Autism: The Facts by Simon Baron-Cohen and Patrick Bolton
Published by Oxford University Press (1993)

Books by people with autism

Cities by Stephen Wiltshire
Published by Dent (1989)

In Dark Hours I Find my Way: Messages from an Autistic Mind by Birger Sellin
Published by Basic Books (1995)

There's a Boy in Here by Judy Barron and Sean Barron
Published by Chapman (1993) ISBN 185 592 634 2

Mental illness and Alzheimer's disease

Living with Dementia by John Riordan and Bob
    Whitmore
Published by Manchester University Press
    (1990)
    Written for carers and professionals by two
    clinical psychologists.

Have the Men had Enough? by Margaret Forster
Published by Penguin books (1989)
    A wonderful novel which realistically
    portrays the feelings and reactions of a
    whole family to Alzheimer's disease. It has
    a background in the author's own
    experience of a family member with
    Alzheimer's disease.

CHAPTER 5

PROMOTING CHOICE AND INDEPENDENCE

This chapter focuses on the practical aids to daily living and the various techniques and therapies which are useful in promoting independence. It also details the benefits available for disabled people and their carers.

Equipment to aid mobility

The ability to move around at home and to get out and about with family and friends is important to everyone and there is a wide range of aids and appliances to help maintain a degree of independence for those whose mobility is restricted.

WALKING STICKS

These are the commonest sort of walking aid and can be made of wood, plastic or metal. It is important that a walking stick is checked to see if it is the correct height and weight and that the shape of the handle results in a comfortable grip. To obtain the correct height, the stick should be measured with the handle on the floor; relax the arm and the tip of the stick should be level with the person's wrist. The end of the stick which touches the floor should be covered in a rubber cap to prevent slipping. Some walking sticks have three or four feet to give better balance by spreading the load (see Figure 5.1).

CRUTCHES

There are two main types of crutch: the elbow crutch and the longer axillary crutch which reaches up to the armpit. Both give more support than a walking stick and allow for the use of one leg only. Modern crutches are designed with specially shaped grip handles which spread the pressure evenly across the hand (see Figure 5.2), avoiding the concentration of blood in traumatised areas that are seen after the use of the older conventional crutch handles.

Figure 5.1   A quadruped (*Extra stability walking stick – Boots*)

WALKING FRAMES

Walking frames are often called Zimmer frames (after the original manufacturer); they offer more stability and support.

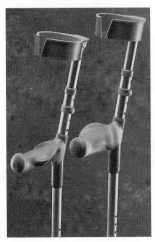

Figure 5.2   Elbow crutches (*Cumfy crutch – Boots*)

There are many different varieties of frame. They can be either fixed height or adjustable; any adjustment should be made by a qualified person, e.g. a physiotherapist. Most frames have four feet (see Figure 5.3); there are also frames with wheels, folding frames and frames with attachments such as shopping baskets (see Figure 5.4). Some frames incorporate automatic brakes which are operated by exerting extra pressure on the handles and a seat for occasional rests. The height, weight and width should all be considered when choosing a walking frame.

CALIPER SPLINT

A caliper splint is an orthopaedic device used to exert control on a deformed leg or to support a leg weakened by a muscular disorder, making it possible for the person

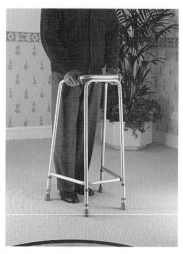

Figure 5.3 A walking frame (*Narrow walking frame – Boots*)

Figure 5.4 A walking frame with wheels, tray, shopping basket and cable brakes (*Rambler – Boots*)

to stand and walk. A person who has lost the ability to flex the foot upwards, for example, will drag the toes on the ground with each step; the use of a caliper splint keeps the foot permanently at right angles to the leg and so enables walking. The splint is made of two vertical metal rods attached to leather or metal rings worn around the limb. The foot end of the rods are fitted into holes in the heels of strengthened shoes. Splints were once widely used to support legs which had been damaged by polio – a muscle wasting disorder prevalent in the 1950s.

WHEELCHAIRS

There are three basic types of wheelchair:

- **Self-propelled**: these have small wheels with castors at the front and two large wheels at the back (see Figure 5.5). The outer rim of these wheels can be gripped by a disabled person to provide

Figure 5.5 A lightweight, self-propelled wheelchair (*Victor lightweight wheelchair, Boots*)

the push to move around; there are specialist wheelchairs for sports use.

- **Pushed**: chairs which are meant to be pushed by another person have four smaller wheels; they may have detachable arms for ease of transfer from bed or car and the tyres may be pneumatic or solid, depending on whether the main use of the chair is indoors or outdoors.
- **Powered**: these are battery-operated and controlled electronically by finger pressure or, if necessary, by chin pressure or breath control. The battery provides power for six to eight hours and is recharged overnight by connection to an electrical outlet. There are several different types of powered wheelchair on the market; those suitable for indoor use are lighter and more compact than the outside models, but they cannot mount pavements and other barriers encountered outside. Chairs suitable for outdoor use are usually wider and longer and are capable of negotiating raised obstructions.

There are also vehicles, such as powered chairs and go-karts, which are specially designed for disabled children. All wheelchairs need regular maintenance and powered wheelchairs need a regular service just as a car does.

When choosing a wheelchair, three factors must be considered:

- **Comfort**: this is very important if the person is going to spend a long time in the chair. Conventional wheelchairs are adjustable: back-rest angle, foot-rest length, arm-rest height, different seat widths and lengths. High performance chairs may offer less adjustment for comfort and tend to be customised for individual requirements. Hand grips need to be tested.
- **Pressure relief**: how much space is there between the back of the knee and the front edge of the seat? A rough guide is to allow at least four fingers width.
- **Space**: where will the chair be when not in use? Must it fit into a car or push right up to a desk at work? What is the narrowest doorway space that might have to be negotiated? Some chairs have quick-release removable wheels and a fold-down seat back. This can be better for disabled motorists who have to pull the chair into the car with them, as taking the wheels off lightens the load considerably.

Wheelchairs are usually supplied through the local Disablement Services Centre (DSC) at the request of an NHS doctor or therapist. If supplied from the DSC, they are on free loan for as long as necessary. They may also be bought privately; places such as the Disabled Living Foundation and Keep Able Centres have a wide range of chairs to try out and trained staff on hand to advise on the best model.

Services to aid mobility

One of the main problems facing someone with a physical disability is transport. The following schemes operate to help disabled people to get about:

- The Disablement Services Authority provides artificial limbs for amputees.
- The Department of Health provides wheelchairs for those who need them.
- The mobility part of the Disability Living Allowance enables some of those with disabilities to put additional state benefit towards the purchase of a car.
- The Motability scheme is a charity run jointly by the government and car manufacturers – its aim is to provide discounts for those with disabilities on leasing or credit purchase of cars.
- Local authorities issue Orange Badges to allow parking concessions for disabled and blind people – either drivers or passengers. About 5 per cent of cars carry these badges.
- Many towns now have a 'Dial-a-Ride' bus service specifically for people with mobility problems.
- British Rail will make arrangements for people with special requirements if given advance notice.
- Most airline and passenger shipping companies have special facilities available for disabled people.
- The Transport Act 1968 gives all county and district councils powers to provide concessionary bus fares for disabled people, although there is wide variation in the concessions offered.
- Disabled people are allowed to use invalid carriages on the footway or pavement, provided that the vehicle complies with prescribed requirements relating to maximum speed, weight, braking systems, etc.
- Some taxi firms specialise in transport for disabled people and hold contracts with local authorities and health authorities to offer the service.
- Travel permits are provided by most city councils and normally allow free travel on railway and bus services; these are usually only available outside peak travelling hours.

ACCESS

While having the *means* to get out and about is very important in the promotion of choice and independence, mobility may still be restricted by lack of *access* to different areas and services. Wheelchair users in particular are not accepted on London's buses and are often excluded from taxis and mini-cabs if they have not already previously checked that the driver will take them. Such restrictions mean that disabled people, especially wheelchair users, are prevented from being spontaneous and from making a choice from the full range of options available to non-disabled people.

activity

Conduct a survey of your local town and find out the following information:

- How easy is it for someone who uses a wheelchair to visit the local theatre or cinema?
- How many pubs and cafes have facilities for disabled people, e.g. ramps, lifts, toilet facilities?
- What car parking spaces exist for drivers with a disability?
- Do the cars using them have Orange Badges?
- Could people with mobility problems use local buses?
- Does the sports centre or swimming pool cater for people with disabilities?

The survey could be carried out by *simulation* (i.e. one student could be in a wheelchair) or by means of a *questionnaire*. If feasible, the trip could be recorded on video and evaluated by the rest of the class.

Equipment for people with visual impairment

There is a wide range of aids to make life easier for blind people and to increase their independence; only a sample of this range is listed here.

STICKS

The traditional long white stick is the item most people associate with blind people. It is useful in that it warns others that the person is visually impaired, and also enables the carrier to tap ahead from side to side and detect potential dangers in the path. Red-and-white striped sticks signify that the carrier has both visual and hearing impairment.

HIGH-TECH 'SMART SPECS'

Star Trek-style 'smart spectacles' could provide kaleidoscopic vision for partially sighted people within the next few years. The University of Bristol's Advanced Computing Research Centre has designed a virtual reality headset, which makes use of the residual colour perception which many registered blind people have; partially sighted people can usually distinguish colour much better than images.

The spectacles are two small liquid-crystal television screens inside a virtual reality headset, with a built-in camera. It is linked to an 'intelligent' computer system (worn as a belt around the waist) which identifies everyday objects and presents them through the virtual reality headset in a graphic montage with colour aids. A simple image of a car parked in a suburban road, for instance, becomes a psychedelic collage of pink cars, orange fencing, yellow pavements and grey roads. It also makes distinguishing the pavement from the road, for example, extremely easy. So far only two-dimensional images can be dissected into regions of colour, and this takes up to 30 seconds to process. The researchers hope to be able to speed up the process, but admit that it will never be an instantaneous process.

LIQUID LEVEL INDICATOR

This device measures liquid being poured into a glass or cup. Two sets of prongs are connected to a bleeper. A short set of prongs measures almost to the top, while the long set measures small amounts in the bottom. A bleep sounds when the liquid makes contact with the prongs.

POCKET WATCH

This watch has strengthened hands and raised dots to make 'reading' the numerals easier for a blind person. There are three dots at 12, two dots at 3, 6 and 9, and one dot at each of the other hour positions.

TABLET ORGANISER

Seven compartments in a strip are each marked visually and in braille (see Figure 5.6). This is a useful memory aid for holidays and a convenient way of packing medication.

POCKET BRAILLE MAKER

This frame produces Braille on one side of the paper. A special pointed stylus is used to make the Braille indentations; a stencil keeps the stylus in the right place, and the Braille can be read without removing the paper from the frame.

MOON WRITING FRAMES AND TEACHING PACKS

Moon is named after its inventor, Dr William Moon; it is a method of reading by touch. Moon letters are made of raised shapes based on the standard alphabet. It is easier to learn than Braille and can be written on special paper using a frame and a ballpoint pen. The RNIB publishes books and magazines written in Moon.

LARGE PRINT BOOKS AND AUDIO BOOKS

Public libraries now stock a selection of books with extra large print and most main libraries also loan audio-cassettes of books and plays. There are also several private companies which offer mail-order services of audio cassettes.

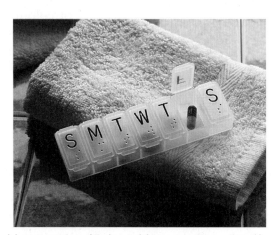

Figure 5.6 A seven-day tablet organiser (*7-day tablet organiser – Boots*)

Equipment for people with hearing impairment

HEARING AIDS

Almost all people with sensorineural hearing loss will benefit from a hearing aid. They can also be helpful for those with conductive loss, for example while waiting to be admitted to hospital for corrective surgery. There are three types of hearing aid:

- **Body-worn hearing aid**: this is often strapped to the person's waist, with a wire connecting it to the earpiece; it is used for profound hearing loss as it enables greater amplification of sound than the smaller devices.
- **Post-aural hearing aid**: this fits comfortably behind the ear; it can also be used with small babies.
- **In-the-ear hearing aid**: these are generally reserved for use with older children and adults.

The aim of all hearing aids is to amplify sounds. In people whose hearing is not helped by such aids, a **cochlear implant** may be considered.

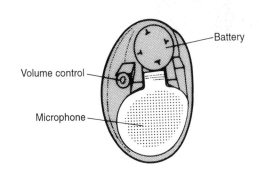

Figure 5.7 A hearing aid

BT HEARING PRODUCTS

BT produces a useful guide for people who are disabled or elderly, to assist them in using the phone. It lists and explains products for people with:

- partial loss and severe loss of hearing
- partial sight and total blindness
- severe deafness and blindness
- restricted mobility

Such products include:

- **Textphones** (not BT): textphones are used by people who are profoundly deaf, hard of hearing and speech impaired to communicate using an electronic keyboard and screen. You type your conversation to another person with similar equipment and both incoming and outgoing conversations are displayed on your screen.
- **Typetalk** (not BT): this is the National Telephone Relay Service which enables textphone users to make calls to or from hearing people. Calls are made via a relay operator who types the hearing person's reply which appears on the textphone. Someone with speech can talk through to the hearing person. Typetalk is run by the Royal National Institute for the Deaf (RNID) with funds from BT.
- **BT pagers**: these receive text messages either via a bureau or direct using textphones; they also have a 'silent' vibrating alert.
- **Videophones**: these provide full motion and colour video, using a special line for handling video and data – the Integrated Services Digital Network

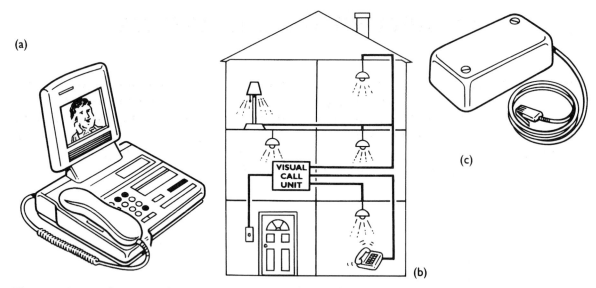

Figure 5.8 Products to aid communication (a) presence ISDN videophone (b) Houselight system (c) Call indicator switch

(ISDN). Videophones are particularly suitable for sign language users.

- **Houselight system**: this makes the houselight flash or dim when the doorbell rings. By connecting a call indicator switch, the lights will also go on and off when the phone rings.

There are many other products and services which are designed to assist people with disabilities, such as sound amplifiers, speech synthesisers, hands-free headsets, and bills in extra large type and in Braille.

SYMPATHETIC HEARING SCHEME

The Sympathetic Hearing Scheme has been introduced to help deaf people and those with hearing difficulties to lead easier lives. The scheme uses an 'ear' symbol. A sticker is displayed in shops or offices wherever someone can take more time to attend to a customer with hearing difficulties. Part of the scheme is to provide anyone who has hearing difficulties with a plastic card with the 'ear' symbol on it.

Figure 5.9 Symbol for the Sympathetic Hearing Scheme

Environmental control systems

These systems are available through the National Health Service and may incorporate loudspeaking telephones to give more independence to people with severe disabilities. They allow external control from a variety of devices by voice or single switch control and are controlled by a computer system. The control system can be programmed to operate door opening and closing; curtain drawing; phone answering; and switching on TV and radio (see Figure 5.10).

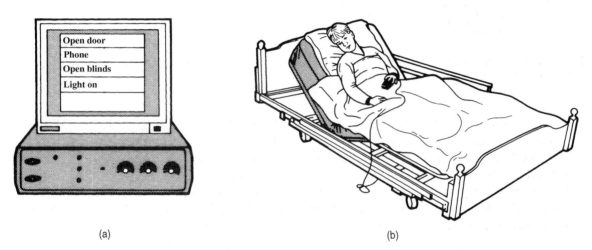

Open door	
Phone	
Open blinds	
Light on	

(a)

(b)

Figure 5.10   (a) Environmental control system (b) User's control pad in operation

Sign languages

DACTYLOGRAPHY OR FINGER SPELLING

People who have a dual sensory impairment, that is they are both deaf and blind, are cut off from the world. Their needs are primarily to find ways to communicate which are purposeful and fulfilling.

Children who attend schools for those who are deaf and blind are often taught by means of dactylography. Dactylography, or finger spelling, would be of little use if the children had little idea about the world and the objects they encounter. Here is an example of how children who are both deaf and blind are taught:

hildren are given a model of a pig ...dle.

2 They then go to a farm and handle a real pig.

3 Back in the classroom, the children use modelling material to make a model of a pig.

4 The children then learn the finger spelling for pig.

Other methods include hearing aids, audiological support, speech therapy and independence training.

BRITISH SIGN LANGUAGE

British Sign Language (BSL) is another name for the sign language for deaf people. It evolved as a natural language and the signs do not necessarily 'translate' directly into spoken English.

MAKATON

The Makaton vocabulary began in 1972 in Surrey as a project to teach sign language to deaf adults who also had learning difficulties. It was later revised for use with children and is now used to stimulate language development in the majority of special schools in great Britain. Makaton provides a controlled method of teaching about 350 signs from BSL. It aims to:

● encourage expressive speech wherever possible

Figure 5.11 British Sign Language (a) positive face (b) watch suspiciously (c) mine (d) thing (e) upright surface (f) flat-sided object.

- develop an understanding of language through the visual medium of the signs
- teach a core vocabulary of a very useful set of concepts/words.

Everyone who teaches and uses the Makaton system is provided with a one-day training workshop and expected to practise signing in order to maintain quality and increase signing fluency.

activity

Find out about the range of communication aids and sign languages available for disabled people in schools and day centres in your area. Examples are:

- Canon communicator
- synthetic speech communicator
- British Sign Language
- Makaton Vocabulary Project
- Blissymbolics
- Signalong

- picture boards
- Rebus reading series.

For each communication aid identified, discuss:

- the ease of learning, both for the teacher and the pupils
- the resources needed
- the type of communication difficulty most commonly targeted.

Utilities and special needs

Service providers of utilities such as gas, electricity and water supplies offer special services for:

- blind or partially sighted people
- people with hearing difficulties
- customers who rely on electrical equipment such as home renal dialysis machines, artificial ventilators or oxygen concentrators.

For blind or partially sighted people
Bills may be sent on an audio-cassette or a friend or relative may be nominated by the blind person to receive the bill and to make payments; special controls such as Braille knobs or controls with raised markings may be provided.

For people with hearing difficulties
Minicom telephones for use with text-phones (see page 149) are available, as is Typetalk. Most utility firms have Special Care Officers who have received training in deaf awareness and some have been trained in sign language.

Equipment to assist with personal care and hygiene

There is a vast range of gadgets and aids designed to increase independence. A few are shown here, but it is worth making a visit to The Disabled Living Foundation or to one of the specialist superstores, Keep Able.

HELPING HANDS

This is a strong, lightweight tool, with an easy-action trigger grip, for picking things up. It has a magnetic tip for retrieving pins or paper clips, and the rubberised tip prevents damage to more delicate items (see Figure 5.12).

Figure 5.13   A tap-turning device (*Easigrip tap turner – Boots*)

Figure 5.12   Helping hands (*Helping hands with cuff support – Boots*)

TAP TURNER

This device helps people to grip and turn taps by providing extra leverage (see Figure 5.13).

KETTLE TIPPER

Any type of kettle can be fitted on to this lightweight balanced platform and

secured by a velcro strap through the handle. It gives the user control and safety when pouring (see Figure 5.14).

Figure 5.14   A kettle tipper (*Kettle tipper – Boots*)

Figure 5.15 A safety cutting guide (*Hold steady cutting guide – Boots*)

Figure 5.16 A bath support rail (*Bath tap support rail – Boots*)

SAFETY CUTTING GUIDE

This device is useful for slicing bread or carving meat. The knife blade is supported and guided by the slots to give the user control and to prevent the knife slipping (see Figure 5.15).

BATH SUPPORT RAIL

This rail fits neatly over standard bath taps to ease the action of standing up in the bath (see Figure 5.16). When not in use it hinges upwards out of the way.

Urinary catheterisation

Urinary catheterisation is usually performed when a person is unable to empty the bladder normally or is suffering from incontinence. The catheter is passed up the urethra into the bladder using an *aseptic* technique (i.e. the creation of a germ-free environment) to protect the patients from infection. If the catheter is to remain in the bladder, a self-retaining type of catheter is used. This catheter has a balloon at its tip which can be inflated and filled with sterile water. The urinary catheter is connected via a plastic tube to a urinary drainage bag, which may be attached to a stand or discreetly strapped to the person's leg under clothing. Although the procedure of catheterisation is performed by aseptic technique, there is always a risk of urinary tract infection. Some people prefer to perform self-catheterisation if they are able; this increases independence.

Housing

Physically disabled people should enjoy the same standard of comfort, choice and independence in housing as able-bodied people. Existing houses and flats are rarely built to meet the special requirements of a disabled person. Under the *Local Government and Housing Act 1989*, anyone wishing to adapt their house or flat to make it a more suitable home for a disabled person can apply for the *Disabled Facilities Grant*. The grant is:

- mandatory, provided certain conditions are met
- intended to provide access to and around the property
- available only after a detailed survey of the property has been carried out – this will assess the cost and extent of the works
- only available to those who are eligible for Housing Benefit.

Sport and leisure

The *Outward Bound Trust* is the largest outdoor personal development organisation in the world. It has 38 centres in 25 countries worldwide. It was originally set up about 50 years ago to promote self-confidence and a will to live in young merchant seamen sailing the gruelling Atlantic convoys during the Second World War. It is the leader in developing courses for people with a wide range of disabilities such as:

- cerebral palsy
- amputation
- blindness
- diabetes
- paraplegia
- deafness
- learning difficulty
- cystic fibrosis.

The Outward Bound Trust also runs courses for carers and works closely with other organisations, e.g. The British Deaf Sports Council, to ensure appropriate programmes are devised.

The Royal Association for Disability and Rehabilitation (RADAR) provides details of all the facilities and access for disabled people at sporting venues. The guide – *Spectator Sports: A Guide for Disabled People* - looks at sports such as football, athletics, basketball, cricket, ice hockey, motor sport, rugby and tennis. There are also chapters on horse racing and greyhound racing. It aims to give the information needed to plan visits to watch sporting events.

RADAR also publishes a *Guide for Disabled People to Historic Buildings of England*, detailing the parking arrangements, internal and external access provision, and availability of facilities such as wheelchairs for loan.

Complementary medicine

Complementary medicine used to be called 'alternative medicine', but most of its practitioners now prefer to see themselves as an addition to orthodox medicine rather than as competitors.

There are some complementary therapies which are well established and provide treatment where orthodox medicine has often been weak. For example, in the treatment of back pain, osteopathy and chiropractic are recognised effective therapies, practised by well-trained professionals. There are other therapies, however, which have less grounding in science and the therapists may not have any recognised qualification. There is no law to prevent anyone setting themselves up in practice as a spiritual healer or an aromatherapist, for example.

There has been a gradual integration of complementary therapies and orthodox treatment within the NHS. Many GPs practise alternative therapies, with acupuncture and homoeopathy being particular favourites. Homoeopathy is the only alternative therapy which is established in the NHS and it is a therapy that does call itself an *alternative* to orthodox medicine.

activity

Find out about some of the more well-known complementary and alternative therapies:

- homoeopathy
- naturopathy
- herbalism
- acupuncture
- rolfing
- reflexology
- aromatherapy
- craniopathy
- chiropractic
- osteopathy.

Divide into pairs for this activity. Each pair should choose one therapy and find out about:

- the principles which underlie the therapy
- the main benefits claimed by the therapy
- the nature of the problems usually treated
- where to go for therapy in your local area.

Put your information into a fact-file for general use by students of health and social care.

Benefits and disability

The welfare benefits system is quite complicated, and finding out what benefits are applicable and then filling in the various forms can be tiring and time-consuming. There are several general guides available from public libraries that explain the relevant benefits in detail, such as *The Disability Rights Handbook* and *Which Benefit?* The Benefits Agency and the local authority will both accept applications made by carers on behalf of the person cared for. They will also send a visiting officer to the home to explain the benefits available if necessary. The allowances relevant to disabled people are changing all the time: some are rolled together, others may act as a passport to other benefits. The actual amounts paid out and allowed as concessions change annually. Some of the benefits available from the Department of Social Security (DSS) are described below and summarised in Table 5.1 on page 162.

ATTENDANCE ALLOWANCE

This is a tax-free weekly benefit paid to those people who become disabled at or after the age of 65 and who can prove that they need to be looked after. There are two rates which apply:

- **lower rate** – paid to those who need attendance during the day (or night) only
- **higher rate** – paid to those who need help both day and night.

The Attendance Allowance is paid *on top* of other benefits. (You have to have needed help for at least six months before being eligible for the benefit.) It is:

- not dependent on National Insurance contributions
- not affected by any savings or (usually) by any income the claimant or their partner may have
- usually ignored as income for Income Support claims.

CONSTANT ATTENDANCE ALLOWANCE

This is an extra amount of money paid on top of war pensions for a disability or illness caused by an accident or disease at work. It is given if the person needs *regular* personal attendance. It is not possible to claim both Attendance Allowance and Constant Attendance Allowance in full together.

DISABILITY LIVING ALLOWANCE

This is a tax-free benefit for people with an illness or a disability who need help with personal care or getting around. It was introduced in April 1992 and is split into two parts:

1 Personal care
This is for people under 65 (but over 16) who need help with personal care. For example, they may:

- need help with washing, dressing or using the toilet
- need someone to keep an eye on them
- need someone to be with them when they are on **dialysis**
- need help with preparing a cooked main meal.

Disabled people may be able to get the benefit even if no one actually gives them the help that they need.

2 Mobility

This is for people over 5 (and up to 65) if they have difficulty in getting around. For example, if they:

- cannot walk at all
- have had both legs amputated above the ankle or at the ankle, or they were born without any legs or feet
- have difficulties with walking
- are both deaf and blind and need someone with them when outdoors
- are severely mentally impaired with severe behavioural problems and quality for the higher rate care component for day and night needs
- can walk but need someone with them when outdoors.

Within the two components, there are different pay scales. This factor, coupled with the obvious difficulties of assessing eligibility, make this a very complicated system to administer. Special rules apply to those who are not expected to live longer than six months because of an illness.

INVALIDITY BENEFIT

This is also a tax-free benefit and is split into three components:

- **Invalidity pension**: this replaces Sickness Benefit after the first 28 weeks of incapacity for work. It is based on having made sufficient National Insurance contributions.
- **Invalidity Allowance**: this is paid on top of invalidity pension, if the disability or illness began before the age of 55 for women or 60 for men.
- **Additional pension**: this is an earnings-related amount starting from 1978. You

can work and earn a limited amount and still be eligible for benefit.

DISABILITY WORKING ALLOWANCE

Disability Working Allowance (DWA) is a tax-free income-related benefit for people aged 16 or over who are working over 16 hours a week or more on average and have an illness or disability which limits their earning capacity. The right to claim DWA does not depend on National Insurance contributions. The amount received depends upon whether the claimant has a partner, how many children are living with the claimant, and how much money is coming into the house each week. DWA cannot be claimed if the claimant and/or their partner has more than £16,000 in savings. Any savings between £3,000 and £16,000 will affect the amount of DWA allowed.

SEVERE DISABLEMENT ALLOWANCE

Severe Disablement Allowance (SDA) can be claimed by those who have not paid enough National Insurance contributions and are thus not eligible for Invalidity Benefit. SDA is payable to those under retirement age. However, people who become disabled after their twentieth birthday can only get a maximum of 80 per cent of SDA. People with disability who are under 19 and in 'mainstream' education may claim SDA, but not if they are in some form of special education.

INVALID CARE ALLOWANCE

This is available for *carers* rather than for

the person with disability. If the carer spends more than 35 hours each week looking after someone who receives Attendance Allowance, they can claim Invalid Care Allowance. The carer cannot earn more than £50 a week after taking off the money allowed for expenses. The sort of expenses allowed are fares or petrol costs to work, something towards lunch and childminding fees. The cost of caring for someone in the household while the carer is at work may also be counted as an expense.

If the carer has a short break from caring, they may still be able to claim Invalid Care Allowance, but the ICA Unit must be informed when a break from caring has occurred.

INCOME SUPPORT

Income Support is payable to anyone whose income falls below set levels. It can only be claimed by those without work or those working for fewer than 16 hours per week. People of working age with disabilities are normally eligible, as they have higher unemployment rates than those without disabilities and, if employed, are likely to be in low-paid employment. The right to Income Support does not depend on National Insurance contributions. Both the carer and the person cared for may be able to claim Income Support depending on the circumstances.

Couples living together as husband and wife are assessed together for benefit. If the person has more than £8,000 worth of savings or other capital, they are not eligible for Income Support. However, if a partner goes to live in a residential home or nursing home, the money savings and any other capital may be assessed separately.

INDUSTRIAL INJURIES DISABLEMENT BENEFIT

For people ill as a result of industrial diseases known to be linked to certain kinds of employment (e.g. asbestosis and silicosis), this benefit is paid on top of Invalidity Benefit. A claimant needs to be 14 per cent disabled to qualify. Related to this benefit are two other allowances – Constant Attendance Allowance and Exceptionally Severe Disablement Allowance.

INDEPENDENT LIVING (1993) FUND

Under Community Care, local authorities have primary statutory responsibility for the care of all disabled people. The Independent Living (1993) Fund works in partnership with local authorities to devise 'joint care packages' that are a combination of services from the local authority and cash from the fund. It can give regular payments to the relative or primary caregiver in order to buy in the extra services needed. To qualify for the Independent Living Fund, a person must:

- be severely disabled to the extent that extensive help with personal care or household duties is needed to maintain an independent life in the community
- be at least 16 and under 66 years of age
- be receiving Disability Living Allowance higher rate care component
- be receiving services to a value of at least £200 a week from the local authority
- have care needs whose total cost to the local authority and the Independent Living Fund is no more than £500 a week

- be receiving Income Support or have an income at or about Income Support level after an assessed contribution is made towards care costs

- have less than £8,000 savings
- have care needs that are generally stable and will be met by the joint care package for the following six months.

activity

There are many regulations concerning *age* which affect eligibility for benefit for disabled people.

1 Draw up a table or chart to summarise which age groups can claim which benefits.
2 Go to your local post office and obtain a copy of the current guide to benefits for disabled people and a claim form for the Disability Living Allowance (Form DLA1 Claim Pack). Fill in the claim form on Roger's behalf (see case study on page 66) and answer the following questions:

Was the form easy to understand and complete?
- What other benefits would Roger be entitled to?
- Was any allowance made for people who do not speak English?
- Can Braille or audio applications be made?

Who cares for disabled people?

In Britain today, approximately six million people are caring for sick, disabled or elderly people on a regular basis, i.e. assisting in some of the essential daily functions. These are the *informal* carers who, rightly or wrongly, occupy an important role in community care. Only a small proportion of people with a physical disability need help with daily living skills, but the vast majority of them are looked after by relatives or friends. They may be a wife whose husband has a physical disability, a daughter looking after her frail elderly mother, or parents caring for a child with learning difficulties. It is estimated that there are around 40,000 young carers, under 18, who care for disabled parents or look after younger siblings. A recent survey by Health Services Management, *A Life of Our Own – Young Carers*, revealed the following facts:

- most young carers were aged between 11 and 18
- more than half of the young people surveyed lived in a lone-parent household, usually with the mother, who was the dependant being looked after
- almost half the dependants had mental health problems
- one of the most common single diagnoses of dependant parents was multiple sclerosis
- much of the care involved personal care

Benefits and allowances	Brief description
Attendance Allowance	A tax-free weekly benefit for people aged 65 or over who need help with personal care because of illness or disability. Day or night or both. Not means-tested. Each person in a household is eligible for benefit.
Constant Attendance Allowance	An extra amount of money paid on top of war pensions and pensions for a disability or illness caused by an accident or disease at work. It is given if the person needs regular personal attendance.
Community Care Grant	A means-tested grant which may be paid to those leaving residential or institutional care to help them to lead independent lives.
Council Tax Benefit and Housing Benefit	These are income-related, means-tested on a sliding scale. Council Tax Benefit is money off the Council Tax bill. Housing Benefit is help with rent or lodging costs. There are exemptions if living away from home, either being cared for or caring for someone.
Disability Living Allowance	A tax-free, not means-tested allowance. It is not affected by income. Must be claimed before sixty-sixth birthday and must have become eligible before sixty-fifth birthday. There are two components to the Disability Living Allowance – Care and Mobility.
Disability Premium	Additional allowance for those receiving Income Support or Housing Benefit. Only paid while person is under 60.
Higher Pensioner Premium	Paid to those who have received the Disability Premium, are still disabled and over 60, or if over 80.
Severe Disability Premium	Paid in addition to the Disability Premium for those living alone, receiving Income support and receiving the Disability Living Allowance above the lowest rate. Note: cannot be claimed if Invalid Care Allowance is being claimed by someone caring for the person.
Disability Working Allowance	A tax-free, means-tested benefit. Must be over 16, disabled and working more than 16 hours a week. It is normally of limited duration (26 weeks) – intended as an income top-up for disabled people who are at a disadvantage in getting a job.
Disabled Child Premium	A benefit for those receiving Income Support or receiving Housing Benefit, if child is receiving Disability Living Allowance or is registered blind. It is means-tested on a sliding scale.

Benefits and allowances	Brief description
Family Credit	A means-tested, tax-free, income-related weekly benefit which is intended as a supplement for those on low incomes with children. It is a passport to other benefits.
Home Responsibilities Protection	Protects pension rights of carers while not contributing because they are looking after someone for more than 35 hours per week for 48 weeks a year. Those cared for must be receiving Attendance Allowance.
Income Support	A means-tested income-related benefit. It is paid to those not working more than 16 hours a week and is intended to make sure that there is enough money to live on. Acts as a passport to many other benefits and allowances.
Industrial Injuries Disablement Benefit	A benefit paid to those who have been injured at work or who have an industrial disease. It is paid in addition to any National Insurance benefit. The amount received depends upon the severity of the injury.
Invalidity Benefit	A tax-free benefit paid when Statutory Sick Pay runs out (after 28 weeks). Premiums for children and other dependants are paid.
Invalid Care Allowance	A taxable and income-related benefit, but not means-tested. Must be of working age up to 65, looking after a disabled person for more than 35 hours a week and earning less than £50 per week after taking off allowances, e.g. for fares, petrol costs, lunch and childminding. Some other benefits are affected.
Jobseeker's Allowance	This replaced Unemployment Benefit and Income Support for unemployed people in 1996. It is not means-tested for six months, but thereafter becomes a means-tested benefit.
Severe Disablement Allowance	A tax-free allowance for those who have not been able to work for 28 weeks but are not eligible for Invalidity Benefit because they have not paid enough National Insurance contributions. Premiums are paid for dependants.

Note: All the leaflets explaining how to claim and the forms needed are printed in English, Bengali, Chinese, Gujarati, Hindi, Punjabi, Turkish, Urdu and Welsh. They are available from Social Security offices throughout the UK.

Table 5.1   A summary of benefits available for people with a disability

such as dressing and bathing, but also physical care such as lifting parents up and down stairs or to the toilet.

THE CARERS RECOGNITION AND SERVICES ACT 1996

This Act aims to make sure that social services listen to all carers and offer the help that they need. Under the Act, carers have the right to ask social services for an individual assessment of the care they provide and of the carer's ability and willingness to continue providing care. Before the carer's needs can be assessed, the person being cared for must have their needs assessed. The assessment is carried out by a social worker who visits the carer and their relative or friend to talk about the sort of help required.

The Carers National Association gives guidelines to carers preparing for an assessment of need:

1 **Housing**: Do you and the person you care for live together or apart? Is this arrangement satisfactory? If not, say why. Are there any particular difficulties for the person you care for in the home for you, e.g. having a bath or climbing stairs?

2 **Health**: Does the person you care for have any health problems which you find hard to deal with? Do you have any health problems (for example, a bad back could lead to you getting lifting equipment)? Are you getting enough sleep? Do you feel as though you are suffering from stress or depression?

3 **Time**: How many hours a week do you care? List the jobs that you do and how long it takes you; include all cooking, cleaning and washing tasks as well as personal care. Have you given up any

hobbies or activities because of your caring responsibilities? When was the last time you had a whole day to yourself to do exactly as you pleased? Do you have to have help during the day, at night, or both?

4 **Practical caring**: Do you have to help with housework, shopping, bathing, toileting, other personal care (such as dressing), keeping an eye on someone, dealing with money (collecting pensions, etc.) and/or laundry? Does anyone help with these? If so, who and for how long? Would you like some help with any of these extra jobs? Prioritise the areas you would most like help with.

5 **Feelings**: What would you most like to change about your situation? Do you feel that you don't have a choice about providing care?

By focusing on the actual day-to-day concerns a carer has, the carer and the social worker can discuss ways in which help can be provided. The assessment of needs will form a basis for the provision of services. Some services available are:

- adaptations to the home and provision of specialist equipment
- a home help with personal care, e.g. bathing and dressing or to do the shopping
- a place at a day centre, and transport to get there
- a meal delivered to the person being cared for, or at a day centre
- homemaker scheme – a volunteer can take over when the carer is ill, so that the disabled person can stay at home and be properly looked after
- permanent residential care
- incontinence services
- help to use educational facilities (such as a college) and libraries

- a telephone
- holidays and short breaks in residential care
- information about what is available and their costs.

All these services are provided under the Chronically Sick and Disabled Persons Act 1970, but the level of provision varies from area to area. Disabled children are assessed under the Children Act 1989 and the Chronically Sick and Disabled Persons Act. The services available under the Children Act include:

- advice, guidance and counselling
- occupational, social or recreational activities such as a playgroup
- transport or help with travel to and from home in order to use services provided
- giving 'assistance in kind or, in exceptional circumstances, in cash'
- home help (which may include a laundry service)
- help to enable the child and their family to have a holiday.

THE DEMANDS FACED BY CARERS

Caregivers and their issues are often overshadowed by concerns about those they care for and the problems associated with that person's illness or disability. Caring can alter a relationship. Sometimes it can bring people closer; other times it can cause a rift. The person being cared for may have very real concerns, such as being a nuisance, frustration at being dependent on someone else, or fear of what the future holds. Some common emotional reactions of carers are:

- **Anger**: this reaction is fairly common; the anger felt by the non-disabled or well partner may be directed towards

healthcare professionals for providing what the carer feels are insufficient answers or inappropriate care. The anger may be directed towards their disabled partner for either creating the situation or for abandoning them. Carers often suppress their anger because they are afraid of what might happen if they let go.
- **Loneliness**: friends of carers often distance themselves to avoid having to think about the same thing happening to them. Carers can feel isolated and believe that no one else could understand the situation they are in. The longer they are cut off from the outside world, the harder it is to take the first step back into society. When caring for a partner, sexual feelings may change. The person's illness or disability may mean that they change emotionally or physically; or the feelings of sexual desire may diminish because of the carer's extreme tiredness and stress.
- **Resentment**: the increase in responsibilities, such as providing or overseeing the provision of care, doing the household chores and often becoming the primary wage earner, leads to resentment. The carer's own needs are pushed to one side as there is less time to attend to them.
- **Insecurity**: the onset of illness or disability undermines a basic sense of trust, leaving uncertainty and anxiety about the future. Will the situation get worse? Will the partner die? Unconsciously, carers may be anxious about who is going to take care of them or their partner if they themselves become ill.
- **Depression**: many carers feel depressed by the enforced isolation and the feeling of not being understood.
- **Bitterness**: the impact of illness and disability continues throughout life, pre-

venting some couples from participating in life stage events, such as having children and sharing activities. This exclusion from life events further separates them from their peers and increases their isolation.

- **Guilt**: feeling guilty is often linked to the fact that carers feel, rightly or wrongly, that they are not doing well enough, or perhaps they are not getting on well with the person they are caring for.
- **Role fatigue**: when illness or disability leads to an individual being incapable of performing certain roles, e.g. those related to employment, house maintenance, self-care, parenting or physical intimacy, the well partner must assume responsibility for them. The result is that the well partner feels overwhelmed, a feeling known as role fatigue. Role fatigue does not get better over time; rather, it gets worse. The stresses involved in the caregiving role tend to be cumulative. In the short-term, carers are encouraged by hopes of improvement or a sense of relief that their partner is alive. As the years go by, home health services may decline and the support from family and friends may lessen; the strain of taking on multiple roles takes its toll and role fatigue sets in.

MEETING THE NEEDS OF CARERS

Recognition of the feelings outlined above is the first step to being able to deal effectively with the stress involved in caring for a dependent person. The Carers Unit of the King's Fund Centre has published a 10-point plan for carer's needs:

1 recognition of their contribution and of their own needs as individuals in their own right
2 services tailored to their individual circumstances needs and views, through discussions at the time help is being planned
3 services which reflect an awareness of differing racial, cultural and religious backgrounds and values, equally accessible to carers of every race and ethnic origin
4 opportunities for a break, both for short spells (an afternoon) and for longer periods (a week or more) to relax and have time to themselves
5 practical help to lighten the tasks of caring, including domestic help, home adaptations, incontinence services and help with transport
6 someone to talk to about their own emotional needs, at the outset of caring, while they are caring and when the caring task is over
7 information about available benefits and services as well as how to cope with the particular condition of the person being cared for
8 an income which covers the costs of caring and which does not preclude carers taking employment or sharing care with other people
9 opportunities to explore alternatives to family care, for both the immediate and the long-term future
10 services designed through consultation with carers, at all levels of policy planning.

activity

Understanding stress in the caring relationship

1 Find out about the long-term effects of prolonged stress on the individual. Discuss the particular stressors that may be present in the caring relationship, both for the carer and for the person being cared for.

2 Find out about the methods used for coping with stress. Two major strategies are emotion-focused coping, using ego defence mechanisms, and problem-focused coping.

R E S O U R C E S

For information on equipment to aid independent living, send for a copy of the booklet *With a little help* . . . from the Disabled Living Foundation; general information can be obtained from the Disabled Living Centres Council (see 'Useful addresses', page 213).

CHAPTER 6

...NT OF SERVICE PROVISION FOR PEOPLE WITH SPECIAL NEEDS

This chapter describes the provision of services in the UK. Statutory (NHS, local authority), non-statutory (local authority, independent-voluntary, private), and informal provision of services for client groups are outlined. Relevant legislation is included relating to access to public services and education. The processes of 'statementing' and arranging a Package of Care are described through the use of case studies, and the chapter explores the way in which such service provision is funded and the difficulties encountered by individuals and groups.

Health and social care is provided through a combination of statutory, voluntary and private organisations, with informal care playing an important part.

- **Statutory**: provided by the state; in health and social care, this means the National Health Service, social services departments run by local authorities, and other local government agencies such as housing departments, education services and leisure services.
- **Voluntary**: also referred to as charities and charitable, non-statutory or non-

profit-making organisations.
- **Private**: businesses set up to provide caring services as a commercial venture, e.g. residential homes for elderly people.
- **Informal**: services provided by family, neighbours and friends.

There have been many changes in the way in which statutory services are provided for disabled people and their carers. The quality and standard of services vary considerably from region to region within the UK.

A historical perspective on special needs provision

It was not until the middle of the nineteenth century that a distinction was made between people with a mental handicap and people suffering from mental illness. The Idiots Act 1886 allowed local authorities to erect special asylums for mentally handicapped people. Those who were physically or mentally handicapped and were unable to be cared for in their own homes were placed in workhouses, psychiatric hospitals and asylums. The terms 'idiot' and 'imbecile' were recognised and acceptable until well into the twentieth century.

Twentieth-century legislation: the main measures

MENTAL DEFICIENCY ACT 1913

This Act reflected the prevailing strong moral outlook of the time, which classed any socially deviant act, such as becoming pregnant outside marriage, as immoral and as a threat to the fabric of society; little distinction was made between those who were mentally ill and those with learning disabilities. Many young pregnant girls who lacked family support were sent to an asylum well away from their home town.

THE DISABLED PERSONS (EMPLOYMENT) ACT 1944

This requires employers of certain sized companies to employ a 'quota' of disabled employees. For companies employing more than 20 people, the quota was 3 per cent. The Act also requires the Secretary of State for Employment to:

- reserve certain kinds of work for those with a disability
- provide sheltered employment to severely disabled people
- provide vocational training – this is usually provided by the local authorities, social services departments or through the Department of Employment rehabilitation centres.

THE NATIONAL ASSISTANCE ACT 1948

This Act compelled local authorities to provide suitable accommodation for all those people who had need of shelter because of age or infirmity.

MENTAL HEALTH ACT 1959

This Act ensured that incarceration because of mental handicap or illness was either voluntary or based on a considered medical diagnosis. The Act also advocated an expansion of community care services, but there was still some confusion between mental illness and mental handicap.

THE CHRONICALLY SICK AND DISABLED PERSONS ACT 1970

This Act was prompted by a government survey which found that at least 3 million adults were disabled to some degree; 200,000 families had a severely disabled member but did not have access to an inside lavatory; and 1 in 5 severely disabled people lived alone without the help of the welfare services. The Act imposed two extra duties on the newly reorganised local authorities:

- to compile a register of disabled people in their area
- to publicise their services.

Unfortunately, the services listed under Section 2 of the Act only needed to be provided where it was 'practical and reasonable' to do so, and many authorities found it was neither practical nor reasonable to provide such services and consequently did not. The services included:

- adaptations to property to enable people to be mobile in the home, or at least to be able to undertake a range of normal household activities
- help in the home
- recreational and certain educational facilities; this covers a wide range of services, e.g. holidays and day centres
- ensuring all buildings open to the public are provided with means of access and toilet facilities suitable for disabled people
- representation of disabled people on

government advisory bodies and local authority committees
- provision of meals.

MENTAL HEALTH ACT 1983

This Act defined mental disorder as a general category subdivided into 'mental illness, arrested or incomplete development of the mind, psychopathic disorder, and any other disorder or disability of mind'. It also laid down rules (referred to as Sections) which applied conditions to the compulsory admission of patients against their will. The role of the social worker was central to the compulsory admission of patients and there was an increased recognition of the legal and social rights of the individual.

THE DISABLED PERSONS (SERVICES, CONSULTATION AND REPRESENTATION) ACT 1986

This Act was designed to give disabled people a greater say in the decisions taken regarding them. Under the Act, people with disabilities have the right to:

- assessment
- information
- consultation
- representation
- advocacy – an advocate (e.g. a social worker) should be present at any meeting where their needs are being assessed.

THE NATIONAL HEALTH SERVICE AND COMMUNITY CARE ACT 1990

This Act has six identified 'key objectives':

1 to promote domiciliary, day and respite services to enable people to live in their own homes, wherever feasible and sensible
2 to ensure that service providers make practical support for carers a high priority
3 to make proper assessment of need and good care management the cornerstone of high quality care
4 to promote the development of a flourishing independent sector alongside good quality public services
5 to clarify the responsibilities of agencies and so make them more accountable
6 to secure better value for taxpayers' money by introducing a new funding structure for social care.

The Act means that the NHS no longer carries the main responsibility for service provision. Local authorities have the major function of providing social care for elderly people, people with physical disabilities and people with learning difficulties. The changes have implications for the roles of social worker and community nurse.

A key feature in implementing the Act is that of *care management*: the central elements of this are assessment and the implementation, monitoring and reviewing of a care plan.

Care plans

All local authorities must appoint a care manager to draw up individual care plans for disabled people in the community and to ensure that the plans are carried out. The development of care plans involves:

- assessing the person's needs
- setting goals
- listing the necessary action to meet the goals set
- if necessary, justifying the actions set.

Care plans may be developed by:

- one professional, e.g. a general nurse, a community psychiatric nurse or other specialist, or a social worker
- a team composed of many different professionals, e.g. nurse, doctor, social worker, occupational therapist and physiotherapist
- the disabled person working alongside professionals; this is one way of empowering disabled people to exercise control over their own lives.

A package of care

The local authority social services department has the responsibility of assessing the needs of the disabled person or family. Once an assessment has been carried out, a person or team is appointed to act as care manager. The manager may be from any of the caring professions depending upon the person's particular needs. The care manager is responsible for the coordination and management of the package of care. He or she is subject to budget constraints and must be shown to provide good value for money as well as meeting client need. Services may be arranged from any available source:

- **informal** – relatives, neighbours and friends
- **statutory** – the NHS, social services, housing, education and other departments
- **voluntary** – charities, housing associations, meals on wheels, etc.
- **private** – chiropody services, taxi services, private residential and nursing homes, etc.

The care manager should be the primary point of contact for both clients and their carers, and the package of care must be based on:

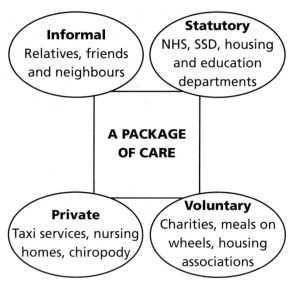

Figure 6.1   A package of care

- an individual's abilities
- the help already available from family and friends
- the suitability of their living accommodation.

Assessment may also involve an occupational therapist, who will advise on any structural modifications necessary, and a physiotherapist who may advise on the purchase of any specialist equipment.

Entitlement to care

In March 1997, the House of Lords ruled that local authorities can withhold or withdraw help from people when short of funds. Organisations representing disabled and elderly people expressed fears that cash-strapped authorities throughout England and Wales would act on the judgement. One man who lost his twice-weekly service was Michael Barry, aged 81. He lived alone, had no contact with his family, and had suffered a slight stroke, several heart attacks, a fractured hip and

sight loss. After his case was taken up by RADAR and the Public Law Project, the High Court ruled that it was right for a local authority to take account of available resources when assessing people's needs and deciding when to meet them. This case and ruling points to the need for *minimum standards* to be applied in all assessments of need. The current law is too vague regarding the services which people can expect when they become dependent on community care.

DISABILITY DISCRIMINATION ACT 1996

The Disability Discrimination Act brings in new laws and measures aimed at ending the discrimination which many disabled people face. The Act gives disabled people new rights in the following areas:

- **Employment**: the Act makes it unlawful to discriminate against a disabled person in the field of employment. Employers will have a duty to provide any necessary reasonable adjustments for disabled employees and applicants.
- **Getting goods and services**: the Act makes it unlawful to refuse to serve a disabled person, or provide a lower standard of service, or offer less favourable terms, because of their disability.
- **Buying or renting land or property**: the Act makes it unlawful to discriminate against a disabled person when selling or letting land or property.

In addition, service providers should:

- amend policies, procedures and practices which make it impossible or unreasonably difficult for disabled people to use their services
- provide extra help and services to help

disabled people get access to their services

- remove or alter physical barriers that prevent disabled people gaining access, or provide the service in an alternative way where reasonable.

Trade organisations should:

- make any necessary reasonable adjustments for their disabled members or prospective members.

The Disability Discrimination Act has been criticised for excluding education from its requirements of service providers.

Skill, the National Bureau for Students with Disabilities, welcomes the long-awaited recognition that disabled people are discriminated against, but objects to the exclusion of education. It is now illegal for a restaurateur to bar a physically disabled person on the grounds that other customers may be upset. But it is *not* unlawful for medical schools to refuse applicants with disabilities, on the grounds that, for instance, they would not be able to keep up with the work; nor is it illegal for a university to reject an application for a degree in laboratory science on the grounds of safety and health hazards.

Services for disabled people

There are a large number of services provided for people with disabilities, but there is considerable overlap and fragmentation. Where these services are well developed, they may include:

- practical assistance at home
- day centres offering activities and companionship
- special education
- support for employment in sheltered and ordinary workplaces
- temporary and permanent residential care

- suitable transport, e.g. through a subsidised taxi service.

In developing countries, where almost 80 per cent of the world's disabled people live, but where only 10 per cent of the resources allocated to disability are spent, services are limited; as in most of the industrialised world, *families* bear the main responsibility for their disabled members.

activity

The statistics in Tables 6.1 and 6.2 were compiled after a major survey of disability by the Office of Population Census Surveys (OPCS) in 1988. Note: the authors of the survey included the category 'eat-

ing, drinking and digestion' because it covered a few relatively uncommon problems which did not result in disabilities covered by the other scales. Consciousness includes the types of disabilities resulting from having seizures or convulsions. Examine the data and then answer the following questions:

1 What is the most common disability affecting (a) children and (b) adults?
2 List some reasons for the differences between the two sets of figures.
3 Figure 6.2 is a bar chart representation of the figures provided in Table 6.2.

Using the data in Table 6.1, draw up a similar bar chart to show the prevalence of disability among children.

4 Represent, in graphical form, the percentage of disabled adults in (a) private households and (b) institutions, for each category of disability.
5 If a similar survey were carried out today, what differences would you expect to find?

MEDICAL SERVICES

Medical treatment is free under the NHS and specialist services are provided for people with specific disabilities, e.g. physiotherapy, community nursing, occupational therapy, speech therapy, remedial gymnastics and dietetics.

REHABILITATION SERVICES

Rehabilitation is the process of restoring a person's ability to live and work as normally as possible after a disabling injury or illness. The services provided may include:

- Occupational therapy
- Physiotherapy
- Speech therapy.

Type of disability	In private households	Total population (including establishments)
Locomotion	9	9
Reaching and stretching	2	2
Dexterity	3	3
Seeing	2	2
Hearing	6	6
Personal care	7	7
Continence	9	9
Communication	10	11
Behaviour	20	21
Intellectual functioning	8	9
Consciousness	5	5
Eating, drinking, digestion	1	1

Table 6.1 Estimates of prevalence of disability among children in Great Britain by type of disability (rate per thousand population)

Type of disability	In private households	In establishments	Total population
Locomotion	4,005	327	4,332
Reaching and stretching	1,083	147	1,230
Dexterity	1,572	165	1,737
Seeing	1,384	284	1,668
Hearing	2,365	223	2,588
Personal care	2,129	354	2,483
Continence	957	185	1,142
Communication	989	213	1,202
Behaviour	1,172	175	1,347
Intellectual functioning	1,182	293	1,475
Consciousness	188	41	229
Eating, drinking, digesting	210	66	276

Table 6.2 Estimates of numbers of disabled adults in Great Britain with different types of disability (thousands)

A new scheme called *Easy Street* has been developed in the USA and Canada. Rehabilitation departments in American hospitals are being transformed into small-scale, highly crafted replicas of their local high street. Shops, banks, post offices, cafés and cinemas are being used to help people to relearn everyday skills in realistic, yet controlled settings. The pioneers of the concept believe that Easy

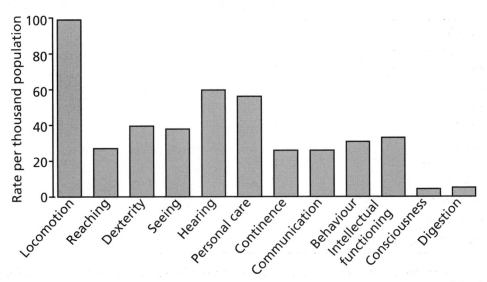

Figure 6.2 Estimates of prevalence of disability among adults in Great Britain by type of disability

Street supplements rather than replaces the use of exercise equipment and allows patients to build up their strength and confidence in an enjoyable therapeutic environment. In the UK, the move has been *away* from using such simulated environments and *towards* sheltered environments.

CONTINUING CARE

Continuing care is the care that might be needed after treatment in a hospital for an illness, injury or existing medical condition. Continuing care might last only a few weeks or months, or for the whole of a person's life. This depends on the nature of the person's illness or disability, and on their particular circumstances. People who need continuing care are usually in one of the following categories:

- adults over 65 with a physical disability
- adults over 65 with a mental illness (including dementia)
- adults aged 18–64 with serious physical disabilities
- children with special needs and disabilities
- people with HIV and AIDS.

Young people with mental health problems and people with learning difficulties are also entitled to continuing care.

Funding arrangements for continuing care

Only a minority of people will have to pay for their own continuing care. The services may be arranged and paid for in the following ways:

- by the NHS, through the person's health authority; this care is free at the point of delivery
- by the local social services department; this care is subject to a financial assessment and may result in the person having to meet some of the costs of care.

Figure 6.3 shows how one health authority allocated funds for continuing care in 1995/6.

Assessment of the need for continuing care is carried out by appropriate health and social care staff, and the needs of carers are also taken into account. A written care plan is produced at the end of the assessment which is intended to reflect the views of the patient and those of their family and carers.

The statutory service providers

THE ROLE OF HEALTH SERVICE PROFESSIONALS

Family doctors

Family doctors (general practitioners or GPs) are independent professionals who are under contract with the National

Health Service but are not employed by it. They are the most available of the medical profession and are also able to refer individuals on to the specialist doctors and to paramedical services.

Physicians

Physicians are doctors specialising in the

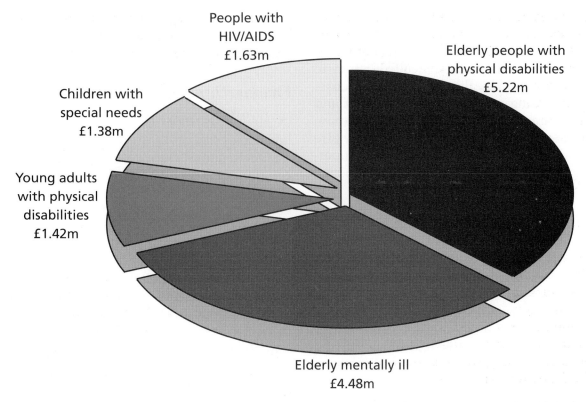

People with
HIV/AIDS
£1.63m

Children with
special needs
£1.38m

Young adults
with physical
disabilities
£1.42m

Elderly people with
physical disabilities
£5.22m

Elderly mentally ill
£4.48m

Figure 6.3   Allocation of a sample health authority resources for continuing care in 1995/6

treatment of diseases under methods other than surgery, e.g. medicines or diets. Every hospital has a number of specialist physicians in areas such as cardiology (heart specialists) and neurology (brain and nerve specialists).

Surgeons

Surgeons are doctors who specialise in direct intervention into the structure of the body. They are also grouped into different specialisms such as orthopaedics (treatment of bone and joint disorders) and ear, nose and throat (ENT) surgery.

Nurses

Nurses work in NHS hospitals and in the community, as well as in private hospitals and nursing homes. There are many different specialist areas in which nurses can gain experience and further qualifications.

Community nurses

Community nurses (or district nurses) work within the primary health care team and their services are arranged through the GP or family doctor. They provide nursing care such as bathing and giving injections and will also show the disabled person how to carry out routine tasks to promote personal independence, e.g. prevention of pressure sores, changing catheters and colostomy bags.

School nurses

School nurses may visit a number of mainstream schools in their health district to monitor child health and development – by checking weight, height, eyesight and hearing, and giving advice on common problems such as head lice. They may also be employed in special schools to supervise the routine medical care of disabled children.

Health visitors

Health visitors are qualified nurses who have done further training, including midwifery experience. They work exclusively in the community, and can be approached directly or via the family doctor. They work primarily with children up to the age of five years (this obviously includes all children with disabilities) and they carry out a wide range of developmental checks.

Care assistants

Care assistants work in a range of settings, but particularly in residential care. They carry out a range of personal care tasks and assist in any tasks which do not require specialist training. Many care assistants take NVQ training.

Physiotherapists

The majority of physiotherapists are employed in hospitals, but some work in special schools or residential facilities. They help disabled people to maintain as much movement and function as possible, using exercise and manipulation techniques. Some physiotherapists work in the community on a peripatetic basis (i.e. working from house to house). They also assess children's motor development and skills and provide activities and exercises that parents and carers can use to encourage better mobility and coordination.

Occupational therapists

Occupational therapists (OTs) work in hospitals, schools and other residential establishments. They also work in the community, employed by the social services department (Community OTs) or for voluntary organisations who cater for severely disabled people. The overriding aim of occupational therapy is to help the person to be as independent as possible. They will assess limitations on physical abilities, and organise appropriate aids, such as chair-lifts etc. They are also trained to help people maximise the physical abilities they have. Some OTs specialise in working with children (Paediatric OTs) and will assess a child's practical abilities and advise on the most appropriate activities and specialist equipment to encourage independent life skills.

Speech therapists

Speech therapists may be employed in schools, hospitals or in the community; some are in private practice. They are trained to identify, assess and rehabilitate people who have language or speech difficulties, however caused. A major part of their role concerns delayed language development in children. They assess a person's speech, tongue and mouth movements and their effects on eating and swallowing. They provide exercises and activities to develop all aspects of expressive and receptive communication skills.

Dieticians

Most dieticians work in hospitals and can advise on a range of special diets, e.g. for people with diabetes or those with cystic fibrosis or coeliac disease. Some GPs employ a dietician to work from the practice and to visit patients in their own homes.

Play specialists

Play specialists are employed in hospitals and are often trained nursery nurses who have additional training. They may prepare a child for hospitalisation and provide play opportunities for children confined to bed or in a hospital playroom.

Play therapists

Play therapists also work in hospitals and have undertaken specialist training. They may be qualified nursery nurses, psychotherapists or qualified as a hospital play specialist. Their role is to use *therapeutic play* with one child or a group of children to enable them to feel more secure emotionally in potentially threatening situations. Play therapy is discussed in more detail in Chapter 4 (page 112).

activity

Try to arrange to visit a children's ward where there is a qualified hospital play specialist or play therapist. Make a list of questions before the visit to find out:

- what activities are used to help children who are in hospital
- what training and qualifications are necessary for work in this field
- what particular needs children and their families have when the child is in hospital.

Write a report on your visit.

THE ROLE OF MENTAL HEALTH SERVICE PROFESSIONALS

Psychiatrists

Psychiatrists diagnose and treat mental illness and emotional problems. Most psychiatrists are based in hospitals, where they are responsible for the care of in-patients and also hold out-patients clinics. In some areas there are community-based mental health centres with psychiatrists attached. They have medical training and are expert in the use of drug treatment; a few psychiatrists also practise psychotherapy.

Mental health nurses

These are nurses who have had special training in psychiatric medicine. They work closely with the doctors and other professionals and are an important part of the team. Their training provides them with the skills needed to communicate with and support people who are mentally ill. They also work with patients in assessing their needs and planning their care, and give medication as directed by a doctor.

Community psychiatric nurses

Community psychiatric nurses (CPNs)

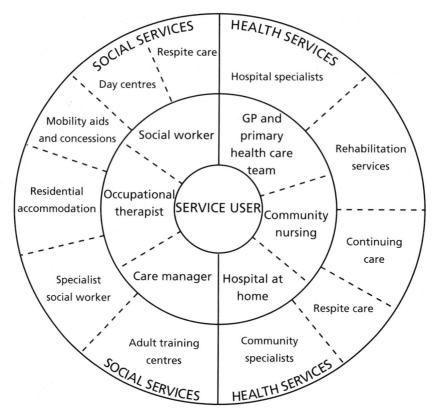

Figure 6.4   An example of services available to physically disabled people

work between the hospital and the community; their main concern is to enable people with a mental illness to remain within the community, or to return to the community following a period of hospitalisation. They are an important part of the team comprising the patient's GP, hospital consultant, social worker and health visitor. They have skills in working with people who have emotional or relationship problems, or who suffer from anxiety or stress; for example, they provide counselling or teach relaxation techniques. Some CPNs have training in specialist areas, such as eating disorders or behavioural therapy.

Mental health social workers

These are social workers who have had training and experience in mental health. They are employed by the local authority in England, Wales and Scotland (or the Health and Social Services Board in Northern Ireland). They work closely with people who are mentally ill and their carers in assessing their needs, planning care and coordinating help. They may also provide counselling, advice on benefits and arranging for day care or supported accommodation. In some areas social workers are known as care managers, although their role does not differ much from that of other social workers.

Clinical psychologists

Clinical psychologists usually work in hospitals. They are not doctors and they do not prescribe medication. Their skills lie mainly in the assessment of mental health problems and in providing talking treatments such as psychological therapies and counselling. Psychologists sometimes also carry out psychological tests, usually in the form of a questionnaire, to assist them in making a thorough assessment of the individual's mental health needs. They may also assess children's emotional, social and intellectual development and advise on appropriate activities to promote development.

Psychotherapists

Psychotherapists other than trained doctors or psychologists may offer therapy in one of the recognised forms of psychotherapy, usually privately. Such therapies are talking treatments and include:

● **Psychodynamic psychotherapy**: this involves regular meetings between client and therapist to explore deepseated problems and the way the client relates to current relationships and early childhood experiences. There are various different schools based on the theories of Freud, Jung and others. The relationship between the therapist and the client is an important tool in

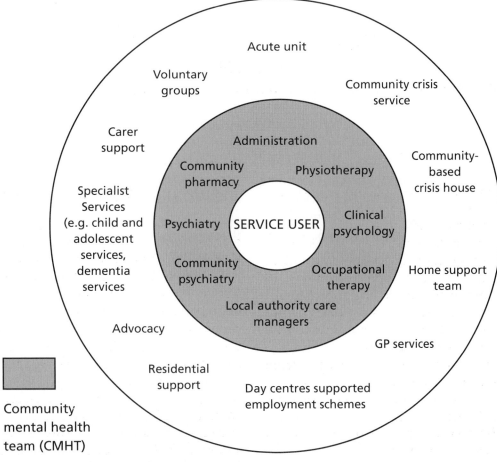

Figure 6.5 An example of organisation of mental health services

developing insight into problems and finding better ways of coping.

- **Systemic therapy**: this involves helping people to see themselves within the 'system' of relationships of which they are a part, and to understand the roles that they and others have taken on. Family therapy is a form of systemic therapy; problems of an individual family member are related to the functioning of the whole family and the therapy involves improving communications and changing unhelpful patterns of behaviour.
- **Cognitive therapy**: this involves help-

ing people by altering thinking patterns which may be at the root of their problems, particularly negative thinking. It may be used in the treatment of anxiety, depression, eating disorders and some of the problems which occur with serious mental illness.

There are many other psychotherapies, including behavioural therapy, transactional analysis, bioenergetics, primal therapy and hypnotherapy. Some may be available within the NHS, but they are mostly practised in the private sector.

WHITE GABLES

Day care provision for people with Alzheimer's disease

White Gables is a day centre for people with Alzheimer's disease in Bromley, Kent. The centre provides day care for up to 25 guests, 7 days per week under the administration of the day care manager. It is open for guests from 8 a.m. to 6 p.m. weekdays; on Saturdays and Sundays it is open for guests from 10 a.m. to 4 p.m. Apart from 'living' rooms and dining rooms, White Gables also has a medical room, used by visiting consultants and for other ancillary services such as chiropody, physiotherapy and hairdressing. There are also rooms for staff and carers' meetings.

A typical day's programme starts with tea or coffee and biscuits on arrival. (Most guests travel in the centre's minibuses; others are brought by their carers). Some guests are given baths at the centre. In the morning, a senior care assistant divides

guests into groups, according to their abilities and preferences, to take part in activities providing some stimulation, for example games or reminiscence exercises. After this, the guests may come together in the lounge to sing or dance, if they are able, or to have a quiz session. After lunch, there may be more activity groups or the guests may come together when one of the volunteer pianists comes to the centre. Guests are also able to sit or walk in the large garden or to play games in the garden when the weather permits. Then there is the return in the minibuses for those using the centre's transport; other guests are collected by their carers up to 6 p.m. Hot and cold drinks are available throughout the day. Staff also assist in the toileting of guests when necessary.

The centre tries to arrange for less

Figure 6.6   White Gables – a day centre for people with Alzheimer's disease

affected guests to come in on Monday, Wednesday and Friday, and for those in a more advanced state of dementia to come in on Tuesday, Thursday and Saturday; different guests come in for different numbers of days per week. The Respite for Elderly Carers at Home (REACH) service can provide respite for a carer from 8 a.m. Friday to 4 p.m. Saturday.

The principles of care

The Alzheimer's Disease Society has developed quality care standards. These are based on three principles:

- **Individualised care**: every person has an individual personality, a history, likes and dislikes, skills and abilities and a huge variety of experience. Care services for people with dementia must be provided in a way that individually recognises and builds on the person's strengths and abilities and maintains their independence; we should not think of people with dementia just in terms of what powers they have lost.

- **Dignity and respect**: those whose mental powers are failing need, in every way, to be treated as a person just as we ourselves would like to be treated. Care services for people with dementia must be provided.

- **Understanding and supporting carers**: a reliable quality service for a person with dementia can provide support and respite from the stressful role of caring for someone with dementia. Care services must have a strong emphasis on carers, using their expertise and experience to improve the care that is offered.

At White Gables, all carers are asked to

contd. ⅠⅠⅠ➡

▐▐▐➡

complete a profile of the person with Alzheimer's disease. The answers to the following questions are used to compile a Personal History Scrap Book for each of the guests. This personal book can then be used to help plan activities and remember, together, the good times:

- Name
- Where they used to live
- Name of wife/husband
- Where they first set up home together
- Names of daughters and sons-in-law, grandchildren, their ages, their home
- Names of friends, any relevant details
- What work did our guest do and any special events they like to talk about?
- What job did their husband/wife do?
- What did our guest do during the war?
- Hobbies
- What sports, teams are they interested in?
- Places of special interest to them
- Anything else we should know which might stimulate interest and bring back memories etc.
- ANY OTHER INFORMATION YOU FEEL WOULD BE OF USE?

- Date and place of birth
- Family
- Where they met
- Names of sons and daughters-in-law, grandchildren, their ages, their home
- Names of close relatives and any relevant details; those that they do still see
- Nicknames or special names used in the family
- Special music that they like
- Do they have any church connections?
- Names and types of pets they have enjoyed in the past
- What are their favourite television programmes?
- Have they ever been abroad? Where?
- Any topics to avoid because of their painful associations

Activities on offer at White Gables

Reminiscence

Reminiscence activities form a very important part of the work at White Gables; this is because the long-term memory of many of our guests is still very clear and detailed, and there are many topics that we can cover. Even in those guests that are less able, we have found that, with appropriate stimulation, they can provide some input to these sessions. Reminiscences are stimulated in different ways:

- by sight – pictures of royalty, famous events of yesteryear, famous people, vehicles, objects, childhood, schooldays, holidays, and everyday life
- by sight and touch – objects used by our guests in their younger lives
- by smell – various scents which evoke memories of days gone by
- by ear – music of yesteryear, wireless theme tunes and programmes.

Orientation

Orientation activities give our guests a

sense of the here and now, and are important in reassuring them about their present situation. Activities include:

- orientation as a quiz game – questions on general knowledge, numbers, letters and day-to-day events
- recognition – recognising simple everyday objects and their uses, or recognising a sequence of events
- word games – Lexicon, Scrabble
- various board games and bingo.

Exercise

Exercise is not only a healthy activity, it also gives us an idea of the guests' overall mobility and spatial awareness. Exercise activities include ball games, such as cricket, bowls, badminton, table tennis and catch, and table games such as bagatelle, shove ha'penny, bar skittles and miniature croquet. All these activities are good ways of prompting upper limb dexterity. In the summer we are able to take advantage of our lovely garden, and we encourage our guests to take an active part in the planning and implementation of the planting in our flower beds and shrub borders. We are also able to use the minibuses to go out on trips, where we can usually find somewhere to walk around.

Social skills

We encourage those guests who are able to involve themselves in the domestic side of the centre. For example, they might practise household skills such as laying up, washing up and putting away crockery and cutlery. We are able to provide cooking sessions, which we have found both our male and female guests enjoy.

Craft work

We recognise the importance of job satisfaction, which our guests certainly enjoy when they are able to complete a craft project. Craft activities include painting, colouring, work with clay, work with paper, flower-making, collages, woodwork, basket weaving and work with felt.

Miscellaneous

- We do a lot of work with music, especially with out less able guests, as we find that they can sometimes respond better to songs than to the spoken word.
- We use jigsaws to promote recognition and dexterity.
- We use smell and touch items to stimulate the senses.
- We give manicures, facials and hand massages to provide human contact.

THE ROLE OF SOCIAL SERVICE PROFESSIONALS

Services provided by social service departments vary from one region to another. A typical range of services includes:

- care at home
- residential care
- social work
- respite care
- foster care
- childminding advice
- equipment and adaptations for disabled people
- adoption
- aftercare for young people
- day care

- nursing home care
- child protection
- disability information, advice and support
- orange badges
- meals on wheels
- help with accessible transport, e.g. taxicard
- bus passes and concessionary travel permits
- support for families.

Social workers

Most social workers now work for specialised teams dealing with a specific client group, e.g. a disability and learning difficulties team. They are employed by the social services departments (social work departments in Scotland) and initially assess the needs of the disabled person. They offer advice on the availability of all relevant local services and may refer the individual or family to other departments such as the DSS, NHS or voluntary organisations. A social worker may act as advocate on behalf of disabled children and adults with learning difficulties, ensuring that they receive all the benefits and services to which they are entitled.

Technical officers

Technical officers usually work with people with specific disorders; for example, audio technicians or audiologists monitor the level of hearing in children as a developmental check. Sign language interpreters translate speech into sign language for deaf and hearing-impaired people.

Nursery officers

Nursery officers are trained nursery nurses who work in local authority-run day nurseries and family centres. Staff are involved in shiftwork and care for children under five whose families may be facing many challenges.

Family aids

Family aids used to be called home helps. They provide practical support for families in their own homes – shopping, cooking, looking after children, etc.

Social Security

There is a wide and complex range of benefits and allowances available to disabled people and their families. Advice may be obtained from social workers or from the Citizen's Advice Bureaux. (Benefits are discussed further in Chapter 5.)

Children in residential care

The Children Act 1989 emphasises that the best place for children to be brought up is within their own families and Table 6.1 (page 174) shows that the vast majority of disabled children *are* living at home. Some residential special schools offer weekly or termly boarding facilities; children may be in residential care for medical reasons or because the family cannot manage the care involved. All homes must be registered and inspected by social services departments to safeguard the interests of this particularly vulnerable group.

Foster placements

The Foster Placement (Children) Regulations 1991 apply safeguards to any child in foster care. Some voluntary organisations provide specialist training programmes for carers fostering disabled children and their active involvement in the child's education is encouraged.

Departmental Structure Chart

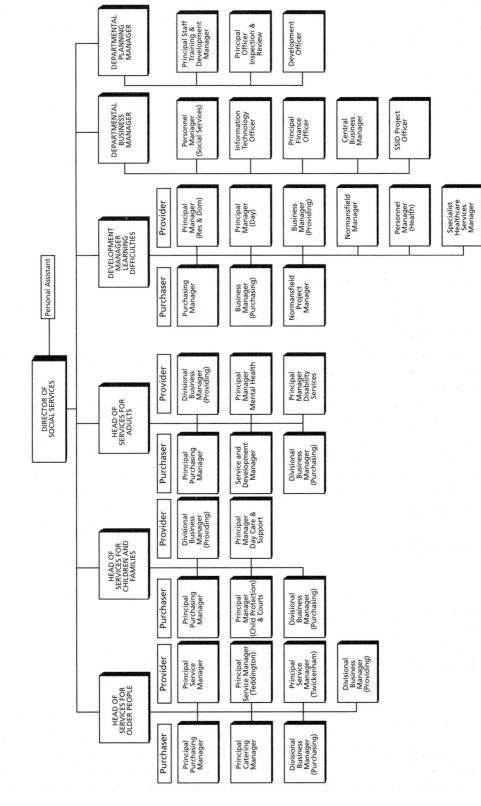

Figure 6.7   An example of the structure of a social services department

Respite care

This should ideally be renamed 'natural break' or 'short-stay' as respite care implies that the carers need relief from an unwanted burden. The aim of such care is to provide support and encouragement to enable the parents/carers to continue caring for their child within the family. There are four types of respite care for children:

- care in a foster placement
- residential care, in a home or sometimes in a hospital unit
- holiday schemes, e.g. diabetic camps
- care within the child's own home.

The latter is often the best provision of care if the right substitute carer can be found. Provision is patchy and is only worthwhile if the child derives as much benefit from the break as do the carers.

activity

Think of ways in which carers of able-bodied children get respite from full-time care. Why can the same avenues not be opened to all carers? List the possible problems for parents of disabled children in obtaining respite care and their solutions.

Adults in residential care

Local authorities have a duty to provide residential care for adults who have:

- **Severe physical disability**: that is, they are unable to manage for themselves with support in their own home and have nobody to care for them.
- **Mental illness**: many large psychiatric hospitals are now closed as the emphasis of care moves towards care in the community. *Joint-tenancy homes* enable people who are mentally ill to live together in a supportive way based on collective decisions and agreements. Some local authorities have *core-and-cluster homes* in which a number of group homes are provided around a central resource from which social work or medical support can be readily accessed.
- **Severe learning difficulties**: the old hospitals which once cared for mentally handicapped people (then called sub-normality hospitals) are being closed and most people who fall into this category have been transferred to smaller community-based residential homes. These homes often have an *independence unit* which consists of a flat for four persons, where the more able residents can prepare for outside living. They are supported in their own management of day-to-day living by a social worker.

Most residential homes provide day care for respective members of the community and also provide respite care so that those caring for them in the community can have a break from care.

THE ANNEXE CENTRE

A day centre for physically disabled people

The Annexe is a resource and activity centre for physically disabled people aged 16–65. It is open every weekday from 9 a.m. to 4 p.m. Clients are usually picked up by the centre's transport or they make their own way by public transport or their own. The centre is run by the social services department and aims to promote independence and to provide enjoyable activities. Some clients attend the centre every day; others come on certain days to join in particular activities. Every week,

staff and clients go shopping to a nearby shopping centre. The activities available are shown in Figure 6.8.

OASIS is a snack bar and shop which is an important social meeting place.
Companion cycling involves the use of specially adapted bicycles for two people, one disabled and one non-disabled. They are not the same as tandem bikes, but can be adapted for most types of sensory disability and many types of physical disability.

Day	Morning	Lunchtime	Afternoon
Monday	'Feelgood' (A session to start the week) Physiotherapy	OASIS (all day) Shopping Aromatherapy	Independent living– promoting independence 1-2-1 Shopping
Tuesday	Craft Furniture restoration 1-2-1 Cookery	OASIS (all day) Fitness and exercise Ten pin bowling	1-2-1 Cookery Flower arranging Photography
Wednesday	Women's Group Art (open session)	OASIS (all day)	Art project
Thursday	Annexe news sheet Physiotherapy Companion cycling	OASIS (all day) Aromatherapy	Gardening Art project Speech therapy
Friday	Douglas Bader Gymnasium at Roehampton	OASIS (all day)	'THANK GOD IT'S FRIDAY'

Figure 6.8   Activities at the Annexe Centre

THE AVENUE

A day centre for people with learning difficulties

The Avenue is a day service for people with learning difficulties. It is open every weekday from 9 a.m. to 4 p.m. and offers a wide range of services (see Figure 6.9).

The purpose of The Avenue, as set out in its mission statement, is to enable customers to realise their own potential and enhance personal growth by actively participating in their local community life. The centre aims to achieve this by:

1 seeking to enhance customers' quality of life by enabling them to explore possibilities, maximise opportunities and develop their own lifestyle

2 enabling people to make choices and decisions, to learn to accept responsibility and to be accountable for themselves and their actions

3 developing opportunities with customers to enable them to form lifestyles through individual interest rather than by a perceived collective disability.

The Avenue has a thriving café and wholefood shop. Each member has a key worker, called a linkworker, who works out a tailormade programme of activities with the member.

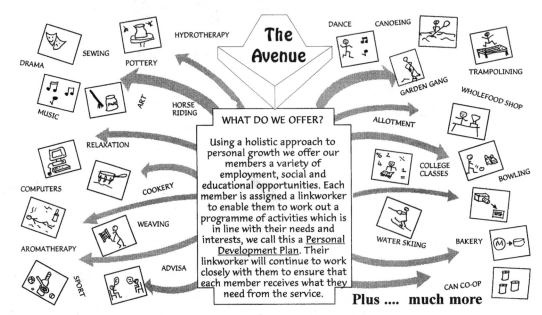

WHO ARE WE?

THE AVENUE SERVICE is a 130 place Social Services day facility for adults with learning disabilities, who live within the London Borough of Richmond Upon Thames.

The Avenue

WHAT DO WE OFFER?

Using a holistic approach to personal growth we offer our members a variety of employment, social and educational opportunities. Each member is assigned a linkworker to enable them to work out a programme of activities which is in line with their needs and interests, we call this a Personal Development Plan. Their linkworker will continue to work closely with them to ensure that each member receives what they need from the service.

DRAMA SEWING HYDROTHERAPY POTTERY DANCE CANOEING TRAMPOLINING MUSIC ART HORSE RIDING GARDEN GANG WHOLEFOOD SHOP RELAXATION ALLOTMENT COMPUTERS COOKERY COLLEGE CLASSES BOWLING AROMATHERAPY WEAVING WATER SKIING BAKERY SPORT ADVISA CAN CO-OP

Plus .... much more

Figure 6.9 Activities at the Avenue Centre. Reproduced with kind permission of Peter Bailey, The Avenue Centre

Key workers

The main responsibility of the key worker in social care is to empower the client. Key workers who work in the community help people to live independently, often in group homes or other forms of sheltered housing. When working with people with learning difficulties, the key worker must:

- help the client to keep in touch with his or her family
- help to order and collect medicines
- help the client to buy new clothes

- organise and attend individual programme planning (IPP) meetings to plan things formally with the client
- communicate with the rest of the team to ensure that the client receives the support and care to which he or she is entitled.

Key workers need to get to know their clients very well so that they can act as a true advocate for them, and so that they can ensure the clients receive the help needed.

activity

Read the person specification in Figure 6.10. Imagine that you are applying for the post of Support Worker and write a list of the qualities you possess that would enable you to carry out the duties of a support worker at The Avenue centre. Write a short paragraph relating to each of the 12 areas of skill, ability and knowledge criteria.

THE ROLE OF EDUCATION SERVICE PROFESSIONALS

Special educational needs coordinators

Special educational needs coordinators liaise with colleagues in special schools and with the parents of children with special needs. They are responsible for coordinating provision for children with special educational needs, keeping the school's special educational needs (SEN) register and working with external agencies, e.g. the educational psychology service, social service departments and voluntary organisations.

Educational psychologists

Educational psychologists are involved in the educational assessment of children with special needs and in preparing the statement of special educational needs. They are *dual* professionals, i.e. both psychologists and experienced teachers. As such, they conduct evaluations of children's educational, psychological and emotional needs, offer therapy and contribute psychological expertise to the process of assessment. Most of their work is with

PERSON SPECIFICATION

Job title: Support Worker – Day Services

Department: Social Services

Division: Joint Services for People with Learning Difficulties

Section: Day Services

The following criteria list the skills, abilities, knowledge, qualifications and experience which we consider are necessary to carry out the responsibilities of the post effectively. Your application will be judged against these criteria and therefore you should address these points when completing the application form. Please note that the application form must be completed in full and that CVs will not be accepted.

Experience

A minimum of six month's experience of working with adults with learning difficulties.

Skills/abilities/knowledge

1   An understanding of equal opportunities in employment and service delivery and its practical application in the context of social care.
2   The ability to demonstrate an understanding of why customer care is important in employment and customer service.
3   An understanding of the needs of client groups.
4   The ability to assess individual and group needs.
5   The ability to respond appropriately to a diverse range of needs.
6   The ability to communicate effectively with a range of people including service users, carers, colleagues, other professionals, outside agencies and the general public.
7   The ability to encourage community presence and community participation.
8   The ability to plan and run groups.
9   An understanding of the importance of supervision.
10   The ability to work as part of a team.
11   The ability to write reports and record information accurately.
12   A willingness to undertake training.

Figure 6.10   Person specification for the post of support worker

children up to the age of 19 who have educational or behavioural difficulties, but they may also be involved in the assessment of, and provision for, children who are gifted and/or talented (see page 117).

Special needs teachers

Special needs teachers are qualified teachers with additional training and experience in teaching children with special needs. They are supported by:

- special needs support teachers/specialist teachers who are often peripatetic, that is they visit disabled children in

different schools and may specialise in a particular disorder, e.g. visual impairment
- special needs support assistants who may be qualified nursery nurses and often work with individual statemented children under the direction of the specialist teacher.

Education welfare officers

As in mainstream education, educational welfare officers will be involved with children whose school attendance is irregular; they may also arrange transport for disabled children to school.

Education

Education is obviously a life-long process but, in formal terms, it involves schooling between the ages of 4–5 and 16–18, with the option of attending colleges or universities or training schemes with an employer.

Until the 1950s in Britain, children born with an obvious disabling condition such as Down's syndrome or cerebral palsy would have been cared for within the family for the first few years of life before being admitted to a large mental handicap hospital where they may have spent the rest of their lives.

Various attempts have been made to define special needs in the educational sphere.

THE EDUCATION ACT 1921

This Act defined five categories of handicap:

- blindness
- deafness
- physical defectiveness
- mental defectiveness
- epilepsy.

Not all children recognised as suffering from one of these disabilities were offered special educational facilities, but many were placed in residential homes for the blind or deaf and dumb.

THE EDUCATION ACT 1944

This Act defined 11 categories of handicap:

- blind
- partially sighted
- deaf
- partially deaf
- physically handicapped
- delicate

- diabetic
- maladjusted
- epileptic
- educationally sub-normal
- speech defective.

All local education authorities (LEAs) were legally bound to provide education for children with such disabilities, although this was not necessarily provided within schools but often as an add-on facility within the large institutions mentioned above. As these institutions or hospitals were nearly always situated on the outskirts of large towns, it was not easy for parents and family to visit the child and often the valuable family tie was broken.

THE EDUCATION ACT 1970

This Act further expanded the previous provision to include those children with severe mental handicap. Such children had hitherto been pronounced 'ineducable'.

THE EDUCATION ACT 1981

Mary Warnock chaired a committee in 1974 which published the Warnock report. The committee's brief was to 'review the educational provision in England, Scotland and Wales for children and young people handicapped by disabilities of body or mind'. The report provided the basis for the 1981 Act. It stated that:

- where possible, children should be integrated into mainstream schools
- assessment of a child's specific needs should be ongoing
- reference should be made to a child's *abilities* as well as his or her *disabilities*.

Special educational needs were defined as mild, moderate or severe. The term 'specific learning difficulties' was introduced for those children who may have difficulty in just one area of the school curriculum (e.g. dyslexia).

EDUCATIONAL SERVICES

The United Nations Educational, Scientific and Cultural Organisation (UNESCO) has estimated that 85 per cent of the world's disabled population reside in nations where few or no special educational facilities exist. Where developing countries do provide special education, it is usually only for children with severe impairments. Cost benefit analyses by UNESCO have shown that, overall, 80–90 per cent of people with learning difficulties are employable if appropriate education and training programmes are completed.

Specialist training is needed to teach special groups, such as those with vision or hearing impairment. Some schools employ peripatetic teachers to work with one child with special needs within a mainstream school.

SPECIAL SCHOOLS

Special schools make up 1.3 per cent of the total school population in Great Britain. Table 6.3 shows the various types of special school available.

CHILDREN WITH SPECIAL NEEDS IN MAINSTREAM SETTINGS

Care and education are difficult to separate, especially when children have multiple disabilities. The move towards

Category	Typical composition of school	% total special school population
Moderate learning difficulties	75–100 pupils on roll Class size 10–12 pupils Curriculum and school organisation similar to ordinary schools, but pupils' progress is slower and they receive more individual attention	52%
Severe learning difficulties	40–80 pupils on roll Class size 8–10 pupils Age range 4–19 years Approximately one-third of pupils have multiple handicaps and there is special equipment Classroom assistants in addition to teachers Full National Curriculum is offered	24%
Emotional and behavioural difficulties	60 pupils on roll Class size 6 pupils Small class size enables teacher to give individual attention and manage difficult behaviour Predominantly boys of secondary school age, although many schools have a small number of younger pupils	8%
Other types Physically disabled Hearing and visually impaired	Varies considerably	16%

Table 6.3   Special schools

Source: Audit Commission

inclusive care and education is one that most parents welcome.

The Children Act 1989 promotes the integration of disabled children in mainstream settings such as nursery schools, day nurseries, schools and family centres. In the United Kingdom, integration is understood to take place at three levels: locational, social and functional.

- **Locational integration** is simply the placement of a child with special educational needs in a unit or class for disabled children in a mainstream school, or in a special school that shares the same site as an ordinary school.

- **Social integration** occurs when the children in the unit/class mix with mainstream children for a range of non-academic activities.
- **Functional integration** occurs when children with special educational needs follow courses, or elements of courses, with their peer group with any necessary support they require.

Mainstream schools will need to consider the specific needs of disabled children in order to promote independence and foster learning.

1 Access

- Specialised equipment such as ramps and lifts for wheelchairs should provide access for all the children in the school.
- Toilet facilities should be large enough to accommodate wheelchairs.
- Computer equipment must have touch-sensitive controls.
- Play equipment should be adjustable, e.g. water troughs that can be set on stands at varying levels.
- Learning materials should be available in audio, large print or Braille for visually impaired children.
- Communication aids such as British Sign Language must be properly taught, as does *any* language if a child is to be supported through it in school.

2 Information

Staff will need information about specific disorders and disabilities in order to plan learning goals which are realistic for the individual child's needs; such information is available from the various voluntary organisations and self-help groups, e.g. The National Autistic Society, The National Deaf Children's Society, The Royal Institute for the Blind and SCOPE.

3 Training

All staff in schools offering inclusive education must be trained in *disability awareness* and *equal opportunities*. Some specialist teachers may be required to work with an individual child; for example, a partially sighted child may work on a one-to-one basis with a teacher who adapts the learning materials being used during lessons.

4 Role models

Children with special needs need *positive* role models. Schools and nurseries can help to improve children's self-image by involving disabled adults at all levels of care and education. Books and activities should be carefully selected to promote the self-image of disabled children – in the same way that the use of multi-cultural resources helps to promote the self-image of minority ethnic groups.

activity

Enabling a disabled child

1 Try to visit a nursery or primary school classroom. Examine the layout carefully. What physical changes would be necessary to include:
 - a child in a wheelchair?
 - a partially sighted child?
 - a child with poor balance and coordination skills?

2 Try to write a story in which a child with a disability is the hero/heroine, but *not* for bravely enduring or overcoming that disability.

THE STATEMENTING PROCESS

Before a statement of need can be drawn up – by a process of negotiation between the education authority and the child's parents – an accurate assessment of the child's functioning and development must be made. Parents are advised to record details of age of developments, e.g. starting to speak, sitting up, crawling, hand–eye coordination; a detailed medical history is also valuable, particularly when statementing applies to a child under four years of age. Statementing is a formal process of negotiation between the education authority and the child's parents. The aim is to identify the areas of need and define the treatment/educational requirements for such needs.

The statement of special educational needs is a legal document which must describe *precisely* the child's individual needs. The Code of Practice introduced in 1994 gives guidance on the procedures. Every school now has to appoint a member of staff who takes responsibility for special educational needs. There are five steps towards statementing, which is only expected to be relevant for 2 per cent of children.

1 The family worker or class teacher, through the observations made in the established record-keeping system, believes there is cause for concern. This concern should be shared with the special educational needs coordinator, and preferably also with the parents.
2 The child is observed and monitored more closely and an individual educational plan is developed with the special educational needs coordinator and the parents: for example, making sure that a child with a serious stutter has plenty of time to talk and chat without being rushed.
3 The school asks for outside help, for example an educational psychologist; a new individual educational plan is drawn up.
4 The procedures for statutory assessment begin. This must take place within 26 weeks.
5 A statement is drawn up.

Features of a statement

- The process may be instigated by the local education authority at any time in a child's school life (i.e. between 4 and 18 years).

- If statementing is required before the age of four, it is undertaken by the health authority. Early education opportunities are usually provided as a result.
- A statement must be updated regularly – generally once a year.
- Extra resources required by children with special needs who attend mainstream schools should be clearly described so that funding is made available.

The statement of special educational needs is in five parts:

1 **introduction** – details of name, address, religion, date of birth, next of kin, etc.
2 **special educational needs** as identified by the education authority
3 **special educational provision** thought to be appropriate to meet those needs, specifying any facilities, modifications to the National Curriculum or specialist equipment
4 **the type of school** or other establishment (e.g. hospital) thought appropriate for the child
5 **any additional non-educational provision** required and which authority should be the provider; for example, mobility aids may be provided by the health authority.

If parents disagree with the statement, they can challenge it. Appeals should be directed to the Director of Education for the local authority. The percentage of children with statements attending mainstream schools rose from 40 per cent in 1991 to 53 per cent in 1995; but support for them there tends to cost more than the specialised staff and facilities available in special schools. Local authorities are increasingly under pressure to cut their expenditure and this can result in widespread variations in the implementation of statements.

THE PORTAGE HOME LEARNING PROGRAMME

The Portage programme was first developed in Wisconsin, USA, in 1970, as a peripatetic learning programme for children with moderate developmental difficulties, in order to overcome the problem of the large geographical distance between families. It has since spread rapidly across the UK and in other countries. It is now the most widespread parental participation programme in the UK and is almost exclusively used by families with children of nursery school age.

The Portage programme works on the assumption that parents are willing and capable of participating actively in remediation and teaching. Here is a typical programme:

1 The home teacher visits the family on a regular basis (usually weekly or fortnightly) at home and sets up a structured teaching programme.
2 The home teacher and the parent jointly assess the child's current level of developmental achievements with the Portage checklist. This checklist underpins the developmental curriculum of the programme and focuses on what the child *can do*.
3 The checklist is used as a basis for deciding on a set of teaching goals.
4 The home teacher shows how a long-term goal can be broken down into smaller, achievable steps.
5 The home teacher then sets up a play/teaching activity to help the child attain a particular step and shows the parent how to carry out the activity through modelling and verbal feedback.

6 The parent tries out the activity in the presence of the home teacher and is shown how to fill in a standard recording form.

7 In between visits, the parent continues the teaching programme on a daily basis with the child.

8 At the next visit, the home teacher reviews the child's progress with the parent, and then decides whether the child is ready to progress to the next stage of the programme.

There have been criticisms of the programme from educationalists. These criticisms centre on the programme's lack of a theoretical rationale for the items included on the checklist, and on the underlying assumption that a child with special needs develops in a similar sequence to a normally developing child. However, the programme is very popular with most parents and is seen by many as an important means of empowerment. The relationship set up between the parent and home teacher has many of the elements of partnership described on page 41. Portage home teachers often act as the family's 'key worker' (as envisaged by the DES Warnock Report, 1978) and provide enormous support and assistance.

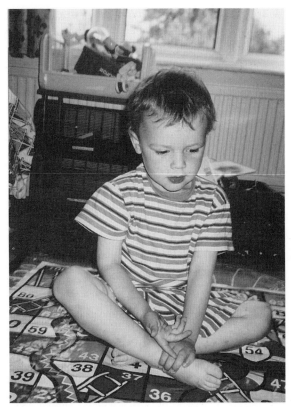

Figure 6.11 Playing at home

FURTHER AND HIGHER EDUCATION

The Further and Higher Education Act 1992 caused a major reconstruction of the way that adult and continuing education was organised and funded. (Scotland was not covered by the Act.) The Act gave colleges independence from local authority control. The significance of the changes for people with learning difficulties were as follows.

Positive aspects:
- with the change in funding arrangements, the number of adults with learning difficulties enrolled on college courses has increased
- there has been a slight shift towards *integrated* learning and away from *segregated* learning.

Negative aspects:
- opportunities for people with severe or complex learning difficulties have been reduced
- help with transport to and from college is still lacking and acts as a major deterrent to the uptake of places
- the new method of funding – the Further Education Funding Council (FEFC) – has vastly increased the

amount of time teachers spend on paperwork and other aspects of administration.

A group of young adults with learning difficulties were asked what they liked and did not like about college; their answers follow:

They liked:
- friendly staff and people
- getting certificates
- good lunch food
- giving suggestions on courses
- staff listening to complaints and taking action.

They disliked:
- verbal abuse
- poor access
- noisy cafeteria
- overcrowded rooms
- poor transport.

Some colleges run a partners scheme, where non-disabled students assist a disabled student for an hour or so each week. This may involve escorting the student between lessons or supporting individuals in, for example, life skills lessons. Disabled students make up only 0.3 per cent of the entire student population in higher education. Most universities and colleges of higher education are very inaccessible, which greatly restricts the choice available to potential students who are disabled.

Employment

The public employment and training services, including those intended for disabled people, are provided by the Manpower Services Commission in the UK, and by the Department Of Economic Development in Northern Ireland.

Certain jobs are reserved for people with disabilities and employers are required, under the terms of The Disabled Persons (Employment) Act 1944 to employ a small number of disabled people (see page 169). Disablement Resettlement Officers (DROs) are employed by the Department of Employment and use medical evidence in order to register people as disabled for employment legislation purposes. In 1991 a new symbol began to appear in job advertisements, shown in Figure 6.12.

Organisations using this symbol must abide by the Code of Good Practice on the

Employment of Disabled People. They are expected to provide all the help they can by:

- providing training
- providing special equipment
- recruiting and retaining disabled people.

Figure 6.12 Equal opportunities logo

The Department of Employment has Placement Assessment and Counselling Teams (PACTS) which offer a comprehensive local service specifically for disabled people. Disability Employment Advisers (DEAs) help disabled people to find work which suits their skills. Assistance available includes:

- referral of job-seekers to an assessment centre or to local specialist training
- advice on aids and adaptations – a free loan service to registered disabled people of certain aids and tools to help them to gain or to keep employment
- Travel to Work Grants – available to registered disabled people who are unable (because of their disability) to travel to work by public transport

- Job Incentive Scheme – employers are given a financial incentive to take on a disabled worker for up to 13 weeks; this offers disabled workers an opportunity to learn a job and demonstrate their capabilities to the employer
- Sheltered Placement Scheme – a wage subsidy scheme aimed specifically to support people who have more severe disabilities who wish to work in ordinary workplaces
- Job Club – offers job-seekers a place to seek vacancies (using telephone, stationery and postage stamps) and a chance to meet other job-seekers.

Remploy is a national organisation which provides sheltered employment for disabled people.

The voluntary sector

Voluntary organisations are *non-profit-making* organisations operating for the public good; other terms used are *charities* or *non-statutory* organisations. Voluntary organisations range from small local support groups (e.g. for blind people) with no paid staff, to large international agencies with paid professionals (sometimes known as non-governmental organisations) such as Save the Children Fund and the World Wide Fund for Nature. There are approximately 350,000 different voluntary organisations in the UK today and about 40 per cent of these are registered as charities. In order to be registered as a charity, the organisation must prove that it meets at least one of the following conditions:

- it must benefit the community in some way

- it must advance religion or education
- it must relieve poverty.

Key features of voluntary organisations are:

- they are not part of the statutory provision of the country
- they may be closely associated with statutory bodies and may receive funding from the state
- it is the organisation which is voluntary, not necessarily the people working for it
- they must not engage in any direct political activity, although many do exert political pressure.
- if registered as a charity, they gain tax relief, rate relief and are able to receive money in the form of covenants at beneficial rates

Agency	Services
Local Education Authorities (Education and Library Boards in Northern Ireland)	• Home teaching/Portage • Nursery education • Statements of educational need (from age two) • Residential schools • Transport to school • Educational psychologists • School-based holiday schemes • Mainstream and special schools • After-school schemes • Educational grants
Social Services (HSS Boards and Trusts in Northern Ireland)	• Social workers • Day care and child-minding for under-fives • Toy libraries • Short-term breaks • Playgroups • Longer-term shared care • Grants and help with transport • Parent support groups • Advice on aids and adaptations for the home • Holidays • Help in the home • Advice on Social Security benefits • Registration on local list of disabled children
District Health Authorities, Family Health Services Authorities, GPs, NHS Trusts (HSS Boards and Trusts in Northern Ireland)	• GP and primary care team • Clinical psychologists and psychiatrists • Physiotherapy • Occupational therapy (also in social services) • Speech and language therapy • Pharmacists • Health education • Short-term breaks, day care and residential care • Home nursing equipment • Incontinence supplies • Specialist Health Visitor • District Nurse • Community Learning Disability Nurse • Clinics • Dentists • Opticians • Wheelchairs, caliper splints, body braces • Mobility aids • Genetic advice and counselling • Child Assessment Centre

Local Authority Leisure Services	• Swimming
	• Play schemes
	• Adventure playgrounds
	• Children's sports activities
Housing Authorities (Northern Ireland Housing Executive)	• Housing
	• Some adaptations to houses
	• Housing Benefit
Voluntary Organisations	• Many of the above services, plus:
	Parent support groups
	Campaigning groups
	Advocacy services
	• Independent advice and information
	• Volunteer home visits
	• Leisure groups (e.g. Gateway leisure clubs run by MENCAP)

Table 6.4 Services which may be available to children with special needs (learning difficulties)

Local Education Authorities Education and Library Boards in Northern Ireland)	● Continuing education: special courses ● Integrated courses ● Education in day centres ● Vocational qualifications
Social Services (HSS Boards and Trusts in Northern Ireland)	● Befriending schemes ● Transport concessions and special arrangements ● Day centres ● Sheltered employment ● Residential care and supported living ● Self-advocacy groups
District Health Authorities, Family Health Services Authorities, GPs, NHS Trusts HSS Boards and Trusts in Northern Ireland)	● Residential, short-term and day care ● Mental health services ● Well-woman and well-man clinics ● Health checks ● Pregnancy and sexuality services
Local Authority Leisure Services	● Adult leisure clubs and opportunities
Housing Authorities (Northern Ireland Housing Executive)	● Council tenancies ● Housing Benefit

Voluntary Organisations	● Many of the above services, plus:
	  Self-help groups
	  Leisure groups
	● Pathway employment and other

Table 6.5   Services which may be available to adults with special needs (learning difficulties)

- they can respond quickly to new needs that arise (the growth in AIDS organisations, such as the Terence Higgins Trust, occurred long before the government began to respond).

VOLUNTARY SUPPORT AGENCIES FOR DISABLED PEOPLE

There are hundreds of voluntary organisations which exist specifically to support people with disabilities. Addresses for further information on specific disabilities and the charities which support them are listed at the back of the book (page 213). Some examples of voluntary support groups are given below.

Action for Sick Children

Action for Sick Children – formerly known as the National Association for the Welfare of Children in Hospital (NAWCH) – offers:

- **family support** – through a national parent advice service and family information booklets
- **information and research** – by publishing and disseminating standard-setting reviews on child health issues, including mental health care, adolescents and the needs of black and minority ethnic children
- **campaigns** – by working at national and local levels to influence policy to improve the standards of health care for all children.

Dial a Dream

This charity was set up to allow children with life-threatening and debilitating illnesses to fulfil their aspirations by making a dream come true. A dream can help them to regain the will to say 'let me live another day', the charity's motto, and give them the strength to face further treatment or hospitalisation. Dial a Dream has organised all sorts of dreams, from meeting the child's favourite celebrity to trips abroad.

Compassionate Friends

This is a nationwide organisation of bereaved parents, who have themselves experienced heartbreak, loneliness and isolation and who seek to help other bereaved parents.

CRUSE

This is a national charity which exists to help all who are bereaved. It offers counselling, advice and information on practical matters and opportunities for contact with others. CRUSE has local branches throughout the UK.

The Child Bereavement Trust

This Trust was formed in 1994 to promote support and counselling for bereaved families. It focuses particularly on providing training for health care professionals in order that bereaved families can obtain the best possible help from their carers.

Contact a Family

Contact a Family is a national organisation which brings together families with children with special needs to provide mutual support and joint representation to health and social care services. It also offers national networks, through meetings, telephone contact and information, for families of children with rare illnesses or disabilities.

RADAR

The Royal Association for Disability and Rehabilitation (RADAR) is a national organisation working with and for physically disabled people. It acts as a pressure group to improve the environment for disabled people, campaigning vigorously for their rights and needs, and challenging negative stereotypes and attitudes. RADAR is particularly involved with civil rights, social services, social security, employment, holidays, housing and mobility. The association offers information, advice and support, and produces informative publications. It also operates the National Key Scheme.

The National Key Scheme

The National Key Scheme offers independent access to disabled people to around 4,000 locked toilets around the country. RADAR prefers all providers of accessible toilets to keep their toilets unlocked if at all possible. The National Key Scheme is suggested only if the provider concerned has to keep the toilet locked to prevent vandalism and misuse. Keys are available to any disabled person for a nominal charge.

Workable

Workable is a consortium of voluntary sector organisations which aims to improve employment opportunities through practically based programmes which open up access to work for disabled people. It offers the following services:

- assessment of the work environment
- assessment of individuals
- disability awareness training
- employee development and training
- graduate support scheme

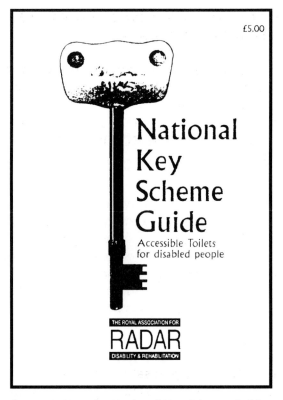

Figure 6.13   The National Key Scheme Guide (published by RADAR, to be updated in 1998)

- new technology information
- staff rehabilitation
- staff retention
- supported placement scheme
- work experience placement
- workforce surveys
- signposting services for information and advice.

MENCAP

The Royal Society for Mentally Handicapped Children and Adults (MENCAP) offers advice and support to people caring for someone with learning difficulties. They produce an excellent family resource pack which includes a list of useful publications on all aspects of learning difficulties.

Association of Crossroads Care Attendant Schemes

Crossroads schemes are available in a number of areas. They supplement and complement statutory provision. They provide care attendants to go into the person's home, helping relieve strain on relatives.

RNIB

The Royal National Institute for the Blind (RNIB) has a very wide range of services for blind and partially sighted people of all ages. It runs special schools and colleges and provides advice and information on all aspects of visual impairment.

SCOPE

SCOPE is an organisation for people with cerebral palsy. It used to be called the Spastics Society. It provides information and advice for people with cerebral palsy and associated disabilities. It runs educational and residential establishments, campaigns for better services and also runs Skills Development Centres to promote empowerment and to help people with cerebral palsy compete in the job market.

National Autistic Society

The National Autistic Society acts as an umbrella organisation to encourage a better understanding of autism and to pioneer specialist services for people with autism and those who care for them. The society:

- runs more than 50 specialist schools and centres around the country
- offers an advice line for parents and professionals
- organises conferences and training programmes
- supports local groups and families
- lobbies to increase awareness, understanding and availability of resources for people with autism.

Alzheimer's Disease Society

The national office of the Alzheimer's Disease Society will provide details of local branches, support groups and carers' contact. Local branches may provide services such as day care or a sitter who will stay with the person with dementia while the carer goes out. A monthly newsletter includes helpful hints on caring and finances, as well as news of research, meetings, local events and new initiatives in the care of people with dementia.

Carers National Association

The Carers National Association aims to help anyone whose life is in some way restricted because of the need to take responsibility for the care of someone else. It provides an information and advice service for carers, including a regular newsletter.

Whizz-Kidz

Whizz-Kidz is a national children's charity whose objective is to enhance the quality of life for all disabled children by providing the best mobility aid for their requirements, whether it be a wheelchair, buggy or trike. It estimates that around 20,000 children in the UK have severe mobility problems; a further 50,000 have problems walking unassisted for any distance. Whizz-Kidz buys mobility aids to meet each child's particular needs, regardless of cost, and makes sure that every child is assessed individually for mobility and seating by a qualified occupational or physiotherapist.

Down's Syndrome Association

The Down's Syndrome Association is the only national charity – covering England, Wales and Northern Ireland – that works exclusively with people with Down's syndrome. It offers help and support to families and carers of people with Down's syndrome and the professionals who work with them. The association produces information on all aspects of the condition and has a resource centre stocked with books, information and videos.

activity

Choose one of the following disabilities to research:

- cerebral palsy
- Down's syndrome
- stroke
- blindness and partial sight
- Parkinson's disease
- multiple sclerosis
- autism
- Alzheimer's disease and dementia
- spina bifida and hydrocephalus
- deafness and partial hearing.

The aim of your research project is to identify the provision of services in your local area for people with the disability.

1 Define the scope of the project and the nature of the disability chosen.
2 Discuss the methods you are going to use to find out:

(a) more about the disability in general
(b) the number of people with the disability in your area
(c) the statutory service provision, voluntary service provision, informal care networks, education, training, employment, etc.

You will need to consult a book such as *Social Trends* or *The Disability Directory* to answer (b), and contact a voluntary organisation, e.g. The Parkinson's Disease Society, to answer (c).

You may decide to design a structured questionnaire to use with a person who has the disability chosen, or to interview a professional working in the area of that disability. The choice of methodology is an individual one, but the information in your project should be thoroughly researched and comprehensive.

APPENDIX 1

PLANNING AND IMPLEMENTING ACTIVITIES WITH CLIENTS

This section of the book gives guidelines for planning and implementing an activity with a client with either a physical disability and/or a learning difficulty. The APIE planning cycle – Aim, Plan, Implementation, Evaluation – is described, and students are encouraged to use a structured step-by-step approach to the activity.

Professionals who work with people with special needs recognise the benefits of providing well thought-out developmental activities. The benefits to the individual or client may include:

- an increase in skills
- an increase in knowledge and understanding
- stimulation
- enjoyment
- a therapeutic outcome
- learning of a new skill
- an increase in self-esteem
- an increase in confidence.

There are also benefits for the professionals, including:

- improved relationships with the client
- improved ability to organise and manage
- increased confidence
- better communication skills
- job satisfaction
- an ability to evaluate their own effectiveness.

Guidelines

The following guidelines should be used when planning and leading a developmental activity with a client.

STEP 1

Choose a client or group of clients with whom to work. The choice may be dictated by where you are able to gain work experience on placement, but ideally will be with children or adults who:

- are physically disabled
- have learning difficulties, or
- are mentally ill.

STEP 2

Identify the needs of the client or group of clients that you have decided to target. Look at the needs discussed in Chapter 1 and list the physical, social, emotional and intellectual needs of the client(s).

STEP 3

Identify the objectives of the activity – for example:

- to increase skills in self-care
- to promote independence
- to improve communication skills
- to stimulate interest
- to provide enjoyment.

Consider what you want the client(s) to develop or achieve. What are the benefits?

STEP 4

Plan the activity. Take time to consider the various ways of implementing the activity. Factors to consider are:

1 Resources
- What materials will you need?
- How much time will you need?
- What information will you need?

- Will you need help from staff or other clients?

2 Contingency plans
Think about what could go wrong or happen unexpectedly, e.g. a fire alarm or a member of staff being away on the proposed day. Have a contingency plan in mind.

3 Roles
Break the plan down into stages and ensure that anyone else involved in the activity knows what their role is. For example, if you plan to use modelling clay in the activity, make sure that someone is responsible – and *knows* that they are – for providing it in the right amount and at the right temperature for use.

4 Monitoring the activity
Ideally, someone will help you by overseeing the activity and checking that it is going well and meeting your objectives. Enlist some help for this aspect, so that you receive valuable feedback after the event.

5 Health and safety requirements
Before using any equipment and materials with the client(s), check with the person responsible for health and safety in the workplace that you are not causing any risk to yourself, the clients or the property.

STEP 5

Explain how clients will be motivated to participate in the activity. Methods you could use include:

- **Instruction**: verbal or written appropriate instructions can help to clarify what is involved in the activity.
- **Enthusiasm**: if you do not appear enthusiastic yourself, you can't expect others to feel motivated.
- **Feedback**: clients will appreciate being

given encouragement in the form of feedback. Genuine appreciation for efforts they have made will help to make the activity a success.

- **Clarity**: clarify activity-related vocabulary or specific terms in context; for example, if you are promoting communication skills through a cookery activity with a group of people with learning difficulties, make sure you explain the terms used in the recipe (blend, sift, knead, whisk, etc.).

STEP 6

Carry out the activity according to your plan or using any contingency measures. Be aware of any health and safety issues you have identified in Step 4. Think about strategies for maintaining interest, particularly using forms of non-verbal communication. Be prepared to make radical changes to your plan in response to clients' needs.

STEP 7

Evaluate your activity. Identify sources of feedback to answer the following questions:

- How did the activity go?
- Was it effective? Did it work?
- What was achieved in terms of your objectives?
- What were the benefits for the clients (those expected and any derived indirectly)?
- What did you learn about the clients? Think about individual responses as well as those of the group.

Suitable methods of gaining feedback include:

- observation – making detailed observations (on audio-tape, video or written) during the activity
- recording client comments during and after the activity
- questionnaire or interview.

Other questions for *you* to answer would be:

- How easy was the activity to implement?
- Was it cost-effective?
- Did it meet the objectives in Step 3?

STEP 8

Make recommendations based on the feedback you have collected.

- Is there anything you would change? Why? How?
- How would you improve the activity?
- Could the information from your activity provide a basis for developing a structured programme to meet clients' needs?

See Table A1 on page 212 for ideas for development activities.

People with physical disabilities, including visual and hearing impairment	*Children:* action games involving appropriate physical exercises; water play; sand play; board games; sorting games; cooking; modelling; musical games; construction activities; art and craft; sensory games, e.g. a 'feely' box with objects of different textures; swimming *Adults:* art and craft activities; cookery; gardening; tenpin bowling; card games; shopping; aromatherapy
People with learning difficulties	*Children:* action games and songs; sand and water play; cookery; modelling; matching games, e.g. picture or sound lotto; sensory games, as above; communication games; jigsaw puzzles; swimming *Adults:* drama; painting; pottery and modelling; music and dancing; cookery; bowling; gardening; shopping; aromatherapy
People with mental health problems, particularly Alzheimer's disease and other forms of dementia	Reminiscence activities; orientation activities; ball games such as cricket, bowls, badminton, table tennis, catch; table games such as bagatelle, shove ha'penny, bar skittles, miniature croquet; craftwork; jigsaws; smell and touch items to stimulate the senses; gardening;

Table A1 Ideas for developmental activities with different client groups

R E S O U R C E S

Play Helps and *More Play Helps* by Roma Lear
Published by Heineman Medical Books
　These useful books provide many ideas for developing play activities with children with special needs.

The Reminiscence Handbook: Ideas for Creative Activities with Older People by Caroline Osborn
Published by Age Exchange.

APPENDIX 2

USEFUL ADDRESSES

Acorns (Children's Hospice)
103 Oak Tree Lane
Selly Oak
BIRMINGHAM
B29 6HZ
Tel. 0121 471 1120

Action for Sick Children
Argyle House
29–31 Euston Road
LONDON
NW1 2SD
Tel. 0171 833 2041

Age Concern England
Astral House
1268 London Road
NORBURY
SW16 4ER
Tel. 0181 679 8000

Age Concern Northern Ireland
3 Lower Crescent
BELFAST
BT7 1NR
Tel. 01232 245729

Age Concern Scotland
54a Fountainbridge
EDINBURGH
EH3 9PT
Tel. 0131 228 5656

Age Concern Wales
4th Floor
1 Cathedral Road
CARDIFF
CF1 9SD
Tel. 01222 371566

Age Exchange
The Reminiscence Centre
11 Blackheath Village
LONDON
SE3 9LA
Tel. 0181 318 9105

AIDS Helpline 0800 567 123
– **leaflets and booklets** 0800 555 777
– **Cantonese (Tues 6–10 p.m.)** 0800 282 446
– **Bengali, Gujarati, Hindi,** 0800 282 445
   Punjabi and Urdu
   (Weds 6–10 p.m.)
– **Arabic (Weds 6–10 p.m.)** 0800 282 447
– **Textphone (10 a.m. to 10 p.m.)** 0800 521 361

Alzheimer's Disease Society
Gordon House
10 Greencoat Place
LONDON
SW1P 1PH
Tel. 0171 306 0606

Association of Crossroads Care Attendant Schemes
10 Regent Place
RUGBY
Warwickshire
CV21 2PN
Tel. 01788 573653

Association for Spina Bifida and Hydrocephalus
ASBAH House
42 Park Road
PETERBOROUGH
PE1 2UQ
Tel. 01733 555988

Barnardo's
Tanners Lane
Barkingside
ILFORD
Essex
IG6 1QG
Tel. 0181 550 8822

The Bobath Centre
5 Netherall Gardens
LONDON
NW1 5RN
Tel. 0171 435 3895

British Association for Counselling
37a Sheep Street
RUGBY
Warwickshire
CV21 3BX
Tel. 01788 578328

British Council of Organisations of Disabled People (BCODP)
St Mary's Church
Greenlaw Street
LONDON
SE18 5AR
Tel. 0181 316 4184

British Diabetic Association
10 Queen Anne Street
LONDON
W1M 0BD
Tel. 0171 323 1531

British Epilepsy Association
Anstey House
40 Hanover Square
LEEDS
LS3 1BE
Tel. 01532 439393

Brittle Bone Society
112 City Road
DUNDEE
DD2 2PW
Tel. 01382 817771

Carers National Association
20–25 Glasshouse Yard
LONDON
EC1A 4JS
Tel. 0171 490 8898

The Child Bereavement Trust
Harleyford
Henley Road
MARLOW
Buckinghamshire
Tel. 01628 488101

Childline
Royal Mail Building
50 Studd Street
LONDON
N1 0QJ
Tel. 0171 239 1000
Helpline: 0800 1111

Compassionate Friends
53 North Street
BRISTOL
BS3 1EN
Tel. 0117 953 9639
Helpline: 0272 539639

Contact a Family
170 Tottenham Court Road
LONDON
W1P 0HA
Tel. 0171 383 3555

CRUSE
CRUSE House
126 Sheen Road
RICHMOND
Surrey
TW9 1UR
Tel. 0181 940 4818

Cystic Fibrosis Research Trust
5 Blyth Road
BROMLEY
Kent
BR1 3RS
Tel. 0181 464 7211

Depressives Anonymous
36 Chestnut Avenue
BEVERLEY
North Humberside
HU17 9QU
Tel. 01482 860619

Disabled Living Centres Council (DLCC)
1st Floor
Winchester House
11 Cranmer Road
LONDON
SW9 6EJ
Tel. 0171 820 0567

Dial-a-Dream
7 Addison Road
Wanstead
LONDON
E11 2RG
Tel. 0181 530 5589

Disabled Living Foundation
380–384 Harrow Road
LONDON
W9 2HU
Tel. 0171 289 6111

Disablement Information and Advice Lines (DIAL UK)
Park Lodge
St Catherine's Hospital
Tickhill Road
Balby
DONCASTER
South Yorkshire
DN4 8QN
Tel. 01302 310123

Down's Syndrome Association
153–155 Mitcham Road
LONDON
SW17 9PG
Tel. 0181 682 4001

Eating Disorders Association
Sackville Place
44–48 Magdalen Street
NORWICH
Norfolk
NR3 1JU
Tel. 01603 619090

Employment Opportunities for People with Disabilities
1 Bank Buildings
Princes Street
LONDON
EC2R 8EU
Tel. 0171 726 4961

ENABLE (formerly Scottish Society for the Mentally Handicapped)
6th Floor
7 Buchanan Street
GLASGOW
G1 3HL
Tel. 0141 226 4541

Epilepsy Association of Scotland
48 Gowan Road
GLASGOW
G51 1JL
Tel. 0141 427 4911

Haemophilia Society
123 Westminster Bridge Road
LONDON
SE1 7HR
Tel. 0171 928 2020

John Groome Association for the Disabled
10 Gloucester Drive
LONDON
N4 2LP
Tel. 0181 802 7272

The Kerland Clinic (Doman–Delacato Therapy)
Marsh Lane
Huntworth Gate
BRIDGWATER
Somerset
TA6 6LQ
Tel. 01278 429089

MENCAP
123 Golden Lane
LONDON
EC1Y 0RT
Tel. 0171 454 0454

MIND
Granta House
15–19 Broadway
Stratford
LONDON
E15 4BQ
Tel. 0181 519 2122

Wales MIND
23 St Mary Street
CARDIFF
CF1 2AA
Tel. 01222 395123

National Association for Gifted Children
Park Campus
Boughton Green Road
NORTHAMPTON
NN2 7AL
Tel. 0604 792300

National Autistic Society
276 Willesden Lane
LONDON
NW2 5RB
Tel. 0181 451 1114

National Deaf Children's Society
45 Hereford Road
LONDON
W2 5AH
Tel. 0171 250 0123

National Portage Association
King Alfred's College
Sparkford Road
WINCHESTER
Hants
SO22 4NR
Tel. 01962 62281

Parkinson's Disease Society
36 Portland Place
LONDON
W1N 3DG
Tel. 0171 383 3513

Partially Sighted Society
PO Box 322
DONCASTER
South Yorkshire
DN1 2XA
Tel. 01302 323132/368998

Play Matters/National Toy Libraries Association
68 Churchway
LONDON
NW1 1LT
Tel. 0171 387 9592

Royal Association for Disability and Rehabilitation (RADAR)
12 City Forum
LONDON
EC1V 8AF
Tel. 0171 250 3222

Royal National Institute for the Blind (RNIB)
224 Great Portland Street
LONDON
W1N 6AA
Tel. 0171 388 1266

Wales Council for the Blind
3rd Floor
Shand House
20 Newport Road
CARDIFF
CF2 1DB
Tel. 01222 473954

Royal National Institute for the Deaf (RNID)
19–23 Featherstone Street
LONDON
EC1Y 8SL
Tel. 0171 296 8000

SCOPE
12 Park Crescent
LONDON
W1N 4EQ
Tel. 0171 636 5020

SHELTER
88 Old Street
LONDON
EC1V 9HU
Tel. 0171 253 0202

SHELTER Cymru
25 Walter Road
SWANSEA
SA1 5NN
Tel. 01792 469400

SHELTER Scotland
8 Hampton Terrace
EDINBURGH
EH12 5JD
Tel. 0131 313 1550

Sickle Cell Society
54 Station Road
Harlesden
LONDON
NW10 4BO
Tel. 0181 961 7795

Stillbirth and Neonatal Death Society (SANDS)
28 Portland Place
LONDON
W1N 4DE
Tel. 0171 436 7940

Sympathetic Hearing Scheme
7–11 Armstrong Road
LONDON
W3 7LJ
Tel. 0181 740 4447

The Terrence Higgins Trust
52–54 Gray's Inn Road
LONDON
WC1X 8JU
Tel. 0171 831 0330

United Kingdom Thalassaemia Society
107 Nightingale Lane
LONDON
N8 7QY
Tel. 0181 348 0437

Whizz-Kidz
215 Vauxhall Bridge Road
LONDON
SW1 1EN
Tel. 0171 233 6600

Workable
Bedford House
125–133 Camden High Stree
LONDON
NW1 7JR
Tel. 0171 267 1415

Internet:
http://www.disabilitynet.co.uk/

GLOSSARY

acquired immune deficiency syndrome (AIDS) A deficiency of the immune system due to infection with the human immunodeficiency virus (HIV).

allele One of two or more alternative forms of a gene in the same site in a chromosome, which determine alternative characteristics in inheritance, e.g. eye colour.

anaemia A condition in which the concentration of haemoglobin, the oxygen-carrying pigment in the blood, is below normal.

attachment An enduring emotional bond that infants form with specific people, usually starting with their mothers, some time between the ages of six and nine months.

attention deficit hyperactivity disorder (ADHD) A disorder of childhood characterised by marked failure of attention, impulsiveness and increased motor activity.

carrier A person who is able to pass on a disease to others without actually suffering from it.

catheterisation The passing of a catheter (a flexible tube) into a body channel or cavity. The most common usage of the term relates to the introduction of a catheter via the urethra into the urinary bladder.

cerebrovascular accident (CVA) The result of impaired blood supply to the brain. Also known as a stroke.

Christmas disease A rare type of bleeding disorder caused by a defect in the blood clotting system.

chromosome analysis Study of the chromosomal material in an adult's, child's or unborn baby's cells to discover whether a chromosomal abnormality is present or to establish its nature.

cochlear implant A device for treating severe deafness that consists of one or more electrodes surgically implanted inside or outside the cochlea in the inner ear.

consultant A specialist doctor in hospital. Working under the consultant are a number of other doctors who are less experienced, but still fully qualified.

CT scanning CT scanning uses X-rays to measure variations in the density of the organ being examined; it compiles a picture by computer analysis.

cycle of disadvantage An assumed cycle in which an environment of poverty and weak education, especially of parents, produces people who cannot improve their position.

cytomegalovirus One of the family of herpes viruses. A pregnant woman can transmit the virus to her unborn child; this may cause malformations and brain damage in the child.

dementia A general decline in all areas of mental ability.

dialysis A technique used to remove waste products from the blood and excess fluid from the body as a treatment for kidney failure.

diuretic Increasing the discharge of urine.

dys- A word element from Greek, meaning disordered, bad or difficult; for example, dysentery = disordered or bad intestines.

dysarthria Imperfect articulation of speech, due to disturbances of muscular control resulting from central or peripheral nervous damage.

dysgenesis Defective development or malformation.

dyslexia A specific reading disability characterised by difficulty in coping with written symbols.

dyspraxia Partial loss of ability to perform coordinated movements.

empathy The ability to try to understand the world from another person's point of view, in order to gain a better understanding of that person.

enema Introduction of fluid into the rectum or back passage.

failure to thrive A term used when a child does not conform to the usual pattern of weight gain and growth.

fragile X syndrome An inherited defect in the X chromosome that causes severe learning difficulties.

genetic counselling Guidance given (usually by a doctor with experience in genetics) to a person or persons who are considering having a child but are concerned because there is a blood relative with an inherited disorder.

haemoglobin The oxygen-carrying substance that is synthesised in the bone marrow for incorporation into red blood cells. Lack of haemoglobin results in anaemia.

haemophilia An inherited bleeding disorder caused by a deficiency of a particular blood protein.

hemiplegia Paralysis of one side of the body, usually caused by a brain lesion such as a tumour, or by a stroke (CVA).

hepatitis Inflammation of the liver due to virus, drugs or chemical poisons.

herpes zoster An infection of the nerves that supply certain areas of the skin (otherwise known as shingles).

human immunodeficiency virus (HIV) The causative organism in AIDS.

hyper- A prefix meaning above, excessive or greater than normal.

hyperactivity A behaviour pattern of certain children who are constantly overactive and have difficulty concentrating on any one activity.

hypertension Abnormally high blood pressure (the pressure of blood in the main arteries).

hypo- A prefix meaning under, below or less than normal.

hypoglycaemia An abnormally low level of sugar (glucose) in the blood.

hypogonadism Underactivity of the gonads or sex glands (testes or ovaries).

hypoxia An inadequate supply of oxygen to the tissues.

ideal self One's perception of how one should or would like to be.

in vitro fertilisation (IVF) Artificial fertilisation of the ovum in laboratory conditions

induction Meaning the medical induction of labour, usually by administration of a synthetic hormone and the artificial rupture of membranes (breaking the waters).

intravenous infusion (IVI) The slow introduction of a volume of fluid into the bloodstream. This method is also known as a drip.

jaundice Yellowing of the skin and the whites of the eyes caused by an accumulation of the yellow-brown pigment bilirubin in the blood. Jaundice is the main sign of many disorders of the liver and the biliary system.

learned helplessness A condition of apathy resulting from experience of no situational control.

lesion Injury, wound or change due to disease in an organ. A local disease condition.

lymph node A small organ, lying along the course of a lymphatic vessel. Lymph nodes act as a barrier to the spread of infection, destroying or filtering out bacteria before they can pass into the bloodstream.

Magnetic Resonance Imaging (MRI) A scanning technique which uses a powerful electromagnet to produce computer-generated images of body organs.

mastery-oriented An attribute of effective learners who accept failure as part of the learning process, who independently correct errors and who set themselves achievable but challenging goals.

meninges The covering of the brain and spinal cord. In meningitis, they become inflamed because of infection by bacteria or virus.

metabolism The chemical process by which food is made available to the body to use.

muscular dystrophy An inherited muscle disorder of unknown cause in which there is slow but progressive degeneration (or breaking down) of muscle fibres.

neonatal Referring to the first month of life.

open heart surgery Any operation on the heart in which the heart is temporarily stopped and the heart's function is taken over by a mechanical pump.

pancreas An elongated, tapered gland which lies across the back of the abdomen, behind the stomach; it has both digestive and hormonal functions.

pilot study A small-scale test of a particular piece of research, in order to test its design and the nature and quality of the data generated.

pre-term Applies to babies born before 37 weeks of pregnancy; full term is 40 weeks.

pressure sores A lesion of surface body tissues due to prolonged or severe pressure inhibiting the local circulation; this usually occurs where tissues are compressed between underlying bone and an external surface, e.g. over the sacrum, on the heels, hips and elbows.

primigravida A woman pregnant for the first time.

protective isolation nursing A technique which provides an ill person with protection from those people who have regular contact, for example a separate cubicle is used in hospital and gowns and masks must be worn before entering the cubicle.

psychotherapy Talking treatment which can assist with a range of problems such as anxiety, depression and mental distress.

recovery position This is a steady position which can save lives, especially when treating an unconscious person or when having to leave one casualty in order to attend to another; it (a) keeps the airway open, (b) allows liquids to drain from the mouth, reducing the risk of inhalation into the lungs, and (c) prevents the tongue from blocking the throat.

rubella A viral infection, also known as German measles. It is only serious when it affects a woman in the first three months of pregnancy, when there is a chance that the virus will infect the foetus and cause any of a range of severe birth defects, known as rubella syndrome.

schizophrenia A serious form of mental illness characterised by disturbances in logical thinking, emotional expression and interpersonal behaviour.

screening The testing of apparently healthy people with the aim of detecting disease at an early, treatable stage.

self-actualisation A term used within the humanistic perspective, by Maslow in particular, to describe the ultimate need for personal fulfilment; self-actualisation involves fulfilling your own potential.

self-concept The idea a person holds about themselves – that is, how they perceive themselves.

self-esteem The overall evaluation a person has of their own worth as a person, based on the qualities that make up their self-concept.

separation anxiety In attachment theory, separation anxiety refers to the unrealistic and often excessive anxiety that a child feels when he or she is apart from the primary caregiver. If excessive, this may develop into various forms of social withdrawal or refusal to go to school.

sphincter A circular muscle that constricts a passage or closes a natural orifice.

spinal cord That part of the central nervous system (CNS) lodged in the spinal canal, extending from the brain stem to the upper part of the lumbar region.

statutory Defined or authorised by statute, or written law.

term A definite period of gestation or pregnancy, meaning full term = 40 weeks.

tinnitus A ringing, buzzing, whistling, hissing or other noise heard in the ear in the absence of a noise in the environment.

ultrasound scanning Inaudible, ultra-high-frequency sound waves are passed into the region being examined to produce pictures of the foetus in the uterus. Ultrasound methods are also used to examine the heart, liver, kidney and other organs.

vertebrae Bones shaped like cylinders which form the spine or backbone. There are 33 vertebrae: 7 in the neck (cervical vertebrae); 12 in the chest (thoracic vertebrae); 5 in the lower back (lumbar vertebrae); 5 fused vertebrae in the sacrum; and 4 fused vertebrae in the coccyx.

vertigo An illusion that one or one's surroundings are spinning, either horizontally or vertically.

BIBLIOGRAPHY

Action on Elder Abuse (AEA) *Hearing the Despair: The Reality of Elder Abuse*. London: Family Policies Study Centre

Audit Commission (1992) *Getting in on the Act: Provision for Pupils with Special Educational Needs: The National Picture*. London: HMSO

Banyard, P. (1996) *Applying Psychology to Health*. London: Hodder & Stoughton

Bowlby, J. (1975) *Separation, Anxiety and Anger*. London: Hogarth Press

Brandon, D. *et al.* (1980) *The Survivors: A Study of Homeless Young Newcomers to London and the Responses Made to Them*. London: Routledge and Kegan Paul

Bruner, J. S. (1963) *The Process of Education*. New York: Vintage Books

Coolican, H. (1996) *Applied Psychology*. London: Hodder & Stoughton

Creschendo, J. (1989) 'I'm in love with my body', in *Johnny Creschendo Revealed*, unpublished

Cunningham, C. C. and Davis, H. (1985) *Working with Parents: Frameworks for Collaboration*. Milton Keynes: Open University Press

Dale, N. (1996) *Working with Families of Children with Special Needs*. London: Routledge

Flanagan, C. (1996) *Applying Psychology to Early Child Development*. London: Hodder & Stoughton

Gross, R. (1996) *The Science of Mind and Behaviour*. London: Hodder & Stoughton

Health Services Management (1995) *A Life of Our Own – Young Carers: An Evaluation of Three RHA Projects in Merseyside*. Manchester: University of Manchester

Hutson, S. and Liddiard, M. (1994) *Youth Homelessness: The Construction of a Social Issue*. London: Macmillan

Keith, L. (1994) *Musn't Grumble*. London: The Women's Press

Langer, E. J. and Rodin, J. (1976) 'The effects of choice and enhanced personal responsibility for the aged: a field experiment in an institutional setting', *Journal of Personality and Social Psychology*, 34, 191–8

Law, J. (1992) *The Early Identification of Language Impairment in Children*. London: Chapman and Hall

Lear, R. (1986) *Play Helps*. London: Heinemann Medical Books

McClelland, D. C., Atkinson, J., Clark, R. and Lowell, E. (1953) *The Achievement Motive*. New York: Appleton-Century-Croft

Mednick, S. A. and Hutchings, B. (1978) 'Genetic and psychophysiological factors in asocial behaviour', *Journal of the American Academy of Child Psychiatry*, 17, 209

Morris, J. (1993) *Independent Lives: Community Care and Disabled People*. London: Macmillan

OPCS (1988) *Surveys of Disability in Great Britain*. London: HMSO

Pringle, M. K. (1986) *The Needs of Children* (3rd edition). London: Routledge

Rosenhan, D. L. and Seligman, M. E. P. (1989) *Abnormal Psychology* (2nd edition). London: Norton

Rutter, M. (1981) *Maternal Deprivation Reassessed* (2nd edition). London: Penguin

Seligman, M. (1975) *Helplessness*. San Francisco: W. H. Freeman & Co.

Selikowitz, M. (1990) *Down Syndrome: The Facts*. Oxford: Oxford University Press

Strauss, A. (1984) *Chronic Illness and the Quality of Life*. St Louis: Mosby

Swain, J., Finkelstein, V., French, S. and Oliver, M. (1993) *Disabling Barriers – Enabling Environments*. London: Sage Publications

Winnicott, D. W. (1958) *Collected Papers*. London: Tavistock

Wolfensberger, W. (1975) *The Origin and Nature of Our Institutional Models*. New York: Human Policy Press

Index